Design of linear
drainage systems

To my son Sajid

Design of linear drainage systems

Matin Naqvi

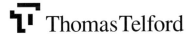 Thomas Telford

Published by Thomas Telford Publishing, Thomas Telford Ltd,
1 Heron Quay, London E14 4JD. www.thomastelford.com

Distributors for Thomas Telford books are
USA: ASCE Press, 1801 Alexander Bell Drive, Reston, VA 20191-4400, USA
Japan: Maruzen Co. Ltd, Book Department, 3–10 Nihonbashi 2-chome, Chuo-ku, Tokyo 103
Australia: DA Books and Journals, 648 Whitehorse Road, Mitcham 3132, Victoria

First published 2003

Also available from Thomas Telford Books
Pipeflow software version 2. (CD ROM). W Chojnacki, S Kulkarni and J Tuach, 1999.
Single user ISBN: 0 7277 2684 6, Multi user: 0 7277 2814 8.
Tables for the hydraulic design of pipes, sewers and channels, 7th edition, 2 vols. D I H Barr, 1998.
Vol 1 ISBN: 0 7277 2637 4, Vol 2: 0 7277 2638 2.

A catalogue record for this book is available from the British Library
ISBN: 0 7277 3222 6

Typeset by Gray Publishing, Tunbridge Wells
Printed and bound in Great Britain by MPG Books, Bodmin

Contents

Foreword

I am delighted to have been asked to prepare a foreword for this unique book.

Highway linear drainage, that is, 'channel with grating', and 'combined kerb and drainage' systems have been used in this country for well over a quarter century. However, apart from a few technical papers and reports, there has been no in-depth work on the theory for surface water runoff in road channels with lateral inflow.

Although, the formuale of varied-flow theory are much more complex than those used by highway engineers for uniform flow in 'pipe and gully' drainage, this book sets out flow calculations from first principles, with many comprehensive worked examples, to assist both students and practising engineers to understand spatially varied flow in linear drinage channels.

Neill Beanland
CEng, MICE, MIHT, DipTE

Preface

This book is intended to guide the reader through the hydraulic design of drainage channels in which the volume of flow increases linearly from one end of the channel to the other. This situation occurs regularly in roof gutters as well as in highway drainage channels, which both receive water from the adjoining surfaces at an almost uniform rate. The varied flow equation, which governs the flow in such channels, has been the subject matter of many books on channel flow. However, the application of the theory to practical designs has been rather limited, due mainly to the equation being complicated, and amenable only to numerical solution.

Accepting the challenge, the author has attempted to outline a negotiable passage that starts with the introduction of the basic hydraulic parameters, covering briefly topics required in the channel flow theory. The text then progresses to verify a procedure for answering the fundamental design requirement of finding the length of a drainage channel or the outlet spacing, and the capacity of a channel with specified cross-sectional dimensions. Any problem areas, such as the location of the control section (see Chapter 8), which need to be considered during the course of development of the procedure have been highlighted, and duly considered. Most of the equations derived in the book are followed by practical examples. The book ends with a chapter on the design of an urban highway drainage scheme that uses the varied flow theory.

As a general rule, in the absence of an exact solution of an equation, the well-known Newton-Raphson method has been used in obtaining a numerical solution of the equation. In some special cases of computing the flow profile, the Runge-Kutta method is also applied. Appendices A and B outline the procedures for applying these methods to the specialized problems discussed in the book.

The references are enclosed within square brackets [$m.n$], where m refers to the chapter where the reference first appears, and n the number associated with the reference quoted at the end of the chapter. The number of references, quoted in the text, are kept to a minimum, and it is expected that the reader will be able to find any additional references for collateral reading without difficulty.

Symbols are defined wherever they first occur. A notation list, containing most of the symbols used in the text, is also given. When a symbol is first set to represent a quantity, it is meant to do so through the entire text. However, there may be exceptional circumstances when a symbol is used to represent some other quantity beside its normal usage. When this occurs, it will be made clear. All quantities are expressed in terms of SI units. All cross-sectional dimensions of channels are in millimetres. The value of g is taken as $9 \cdot 806 \, \text{m/s}^2$ throughout the text.

The author thanks many friends who have been most helpful during the course of preparing the book, and in particular, Neill Beanland (inventor of the Beany block, a combined kerb-drainage system) for his support and valuable criticism, Dr J.C. Boot, Reader in the School of Engineering, Design and Technology, University of Bradford, for his interest and encouragement during the course of writing. Thanks are also due to Steven Barker for digitizing some essential photographs included in the text. Most importantly, the School of Engineering, Design and Technology, University of Bradford provided all facilities required in the preparation of the manuscript, for which the author is most grateful.

The author also wishes to thank his dear wife Zeenat for her undiminished and most loving support throughout the writing of the book.

Acknowledgements

The author wishes to acknowledge with thanks, Marshalls of Halifax (West Yorkshire) for the supply of photographs that appear as Figs 1.2 and 1.4; Wallingford Hydraulic Station for allowing reproduction of Figs 6.1–6.4 of its publication *Design and Analysis of Urban Drainage: The Wallingford Procedure.* These appear here as Figs 1.9–1.12; British Standards Institution for allowing the inclusion of Fig. 21 of BS 6367, which appears as Fig. 9.1; Highways Section, Department of Transportation, Design and Planning, Bradford Metropolitan District Council, West Yorkshire, for details of a proposed drainage scheme.

Notation

Properties of catchment area

C_r runoff coefficient
A surface area to be drained
I intensity of rainfall

Geometrical properties of flow

y depth of flow, measured vertically above the channel bed
h available depth of channel
y_c critical depth
d diameter of circular pipe $= 2a$
θ half of the angle subtended by wetted perimeter
θ_c critical value of θ
A area of cross section
P wetted perimeter
R hydraulic radius
D hydraulic depth
B base width
T top width
m_1, m_2 side slopes (triangular and trapezoidal channels)
L length of channel

Material properties of flow

ρ mass density
γ unit weight
μ dynamic viscosity
η kinematic viscosity

Dynamics of flow

x distance from upstream end of channel
ζ apparent coefficient of viscosity (eddy viscosity)

u, v	streamline-velocity components
u_*	shear velocity
U	mean velocity of flow
Q	rate of discharge
S_0	bed slope (channel gradient)
S_f	friction slope
S_c	critical slope
τ	shear stress
k_s	height of equivalent sand roughness
f and λ	coefficients of friction
F	force acting on an elementary volume of flow
E	energy per unit volume of flow
e	specific energy of flow
H	total head
n	Manning's roughness factor
C	Chezy's coefficient of friction
h_f	head loss due to friction
l	mixing length
R	Reynolds number
F	Froude number

Design of drainage systems

S_c	cross fall of road surface
W_f	width of flow in a conventional drainage system
W_e	effective width of catchment area
A_d	area to be drained
A_a	actual area drained by the drainage system
T	time of concentration (not to be confused with the top width of flow)

1

Flow in drainage systems

This chapter outlines the basic design requirements of surface drainage systems, with special reference to the traditionally applied open channels, and the more recently introduced linear drainage channels. Since the adequacy of both systems requires an efficient transportation of rainwater from the area to be drained, the chapter includes the two prevailing methods for calculating the rainfall runoff, the Lloyd-Davies formula, and the Wallingford procedure, with examples to illustrate their application.

1.1 Highway drainage systems

The need for removal of storm water from road surfaces was realized during early days of road construction. Romans, for instance, introduced drainage to their road systems. Later, industrial advancement required raising the standard of highways, which could not be achieved without incorporating an efficient method of disposal of surface water, in addition to cambering the road. Thus a *surface drainage system* became a necessity, and its design is now an integral part of modern highway design.

The traditional, and still vastly popular, method for the disposal of surplus water from road surfaces is by means of open channels built adjacent to the kerb. These channels are preferably triangular, with the kerb face as the vertical side, and a limited width of the carriageway, with a certain amount of cross fall, as the sloping side (Fig. 1.1). Other shapes, such as rectangular or trapezoidal, are less common. The allowable width of flow that can be allowed in roadside channels is normally governed by the safety requirements, and depends on the type of road construction. For instance, in trunk roads it should not exceed 1·5 m if there is a hard shoulder, and 1·0 m if there is a hard strip. For shopping precincts the value is limited to 0·5 m. The limitation on the width of flow restricts the cross-sectional area of flow. Hence, in order to keep the area of cross section of flow within the prescribed limits, the flow in the channel has to be intercepted, at appropriate points, by means of gullies

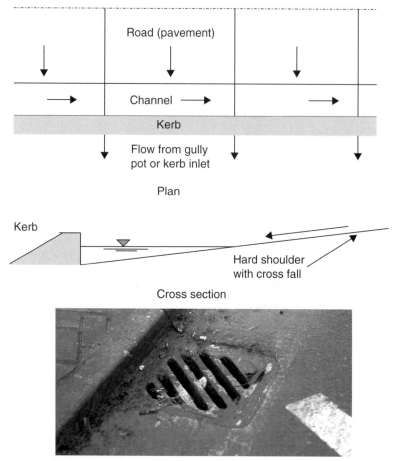

Figure 1.1 *A conventional drainage system.*

with grated tops, or by openings in the kerb, called kerb inlets. In this way, the water is removed from the road surface, and is directed, sometimes through French drains, to a receiving channel that may be, for instance, a natural watercourse in the countryside, or a specially designed storm sewer in the urban area (see Chapter 5 of reference [1.1]).

An alternative system of drainage that is becoming popular is the *linear drainage system*. Linear drainage channels are closed conduits, constructed by assembling precast units, and admit water through an inlet mechanism incorporated into the system. A linear drainage channel may be one of the following two types:

(a) Channels with grated top, flush with the road surface (Fig. 1.2). Such a channel is made of precast units, each of length of the order of

Figure 1.2 *A linear drainage channel with grated top.*

0·5 to 1·0 m, and of the cross section, preferably, either circular with a vertical neck, or of a U shape (Fig. 1.3).

(b) Channels combined with the kerb, the so-called *combined kerb-drainage channels* (Fig. 1.4). Such a channel is also made of units of the same length as in (a) above, and manufactured in variously shaped cross sections.

Each unit of a combined system consists of two parts, the top and the base blocks (Fig. 1.5). An orifice, to allow free access of water into the channel, is located in the top block. At a pedestrian crossing, the kerb is dropped, and the top block dispensed with. In this situation, only the base block provides the necessary drainage capacity (see Chapter 11).

The depth of flow in a linear drainage channel is also restricted by the available depth of the channel, requiring the flow to leave the channel at suitably located outfalls, and conveyed to a receiving channel. Thus, the outfalls of a linear drainage system serve the same purpose as the gullies of the traditional system. The growing popularity of linear drainage systems is mainly due to their requirement of less amount of excavation and, possibly, minimum obstruction with the services. A linear drainage system is also more flexible in the sense that it is applicable to large paved areas

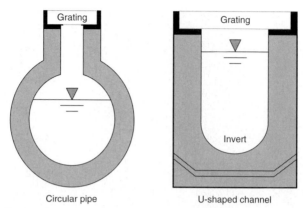

Figure 1.3 *Preferred cross sections for linear drainage channels of type (a) with grated tops.*

Figure 1.4 *A combined kerb-drainage system of type (b).*

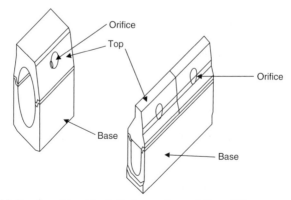

Figure 1.5 *Units of combined kerb-drainage channel (type (b)).*

Figure 1.6 *A roof gutter with two vertical outlet-pipes.*

such as motorways and airport runways, as well as to restricted areas such as car parks and shopping precincts.

The method of computing flow in linear drainage systems also applies to roof gutters. A roof gutter (Fig. 1.6) admits rainwater from the roof surface at a uniform rate over its entire length and, hence, the rate of discharge increases linearly along the length of the gutter.

1.2 Design criteria of drainage systems

The basic design requirement of a drainage system is to maintain balance between the volume of water to be removed, and the flow-carrying capacity of the system. The volume of water required to be removed by a drainage channel is routinely determined from the runoff formula of the type

$$Q_{max} = \frac{C_r I A_s}{36 \times 10^5} \tag{1.1}$$

where C_r = coefficient of runoff, I = average intensity of rainfall (mm/hr), A_s = surface area to be drained (m^2), and Q_{max} = rate of discharge (m^3/s).

The coefficient of runoff is the ratio of the volume of water actually transported by the drainage channel to the total amount of rainfall on the surface, and its value depends on the permeability of the surface to be drained. In the case of an impervious surface, the coefficient of runoff may represent the loss of water due, for instance, to cracks in the surface, and ponding.

A typical urban drainage scheme consists of a main channel, which is usually a pipe, with several tributary channels. The total area to be drained is divided into sub-areas, each sub-area acting as a catchment area for a *pipe length* that is defined by a manhole at each end. Hence, the only parameter in Eq. (1.1) to be determined by external means is the intensity of rainfall. This is discussed in the following section. In a highway drainage scheme, the area to be drained depends on the length of the drainage channel, which is, generally, not known at the start of the computation. Hence, there is an element of trial and error in computing the area to be drained, and the volume of flow to be carried by the channel. This is dealt with in Chapter 9.

It has been common practice to design a highway drainage system on the assumption that the drainage channel flows full, that is, it occupies the available area of cross section entirely. This allows the condition of uniform flow to prevail (see Chapter 3), and the discharge-carrying capacity of the channel is obtained by multiplying the mean velocity of flow with the area of cross section of the channel. One implication of this method is that the capacity of the channel is independent of the length of the channel, which is not the case of a linear drainage channel.

In the event of rainfall, there is a regular inflow of water into the channel, causing the rate of flow in the channel to rise, usually, from zero at the upstream end, to a maximum value at the downstream end. The increase in discharge causes both the depth and velocity of flow to also vary, notably, if the channel is of constant cross section. The *varied-flow theory* takes this into consideration. The theory assumes, however, that the flow entering the channel laterally is constant, that is, the rate of the longitudinal flow increases linearly.

In a normal situation, there is no lateral inflow at the upstream end of a drainage channel, so that the discharge rate Q at a distance x from the upstream end is given by the equation

$$Q = Q_0 \frac{x}{L} \tag{1.2}$$

where L is the length of the channel, and Q_0 is the discharge at the downstream end of the channel (Fig. 1.7).

If U_0 and A_0 are, respectively, the velocity and the cross-sectional area of flow at the outlet, then the capacity of the channel Q_0 is defined by the equation

$$Q_0 = U_0 A_0 \tag{1.3}$$

Hence, the above-mentioned balance between the volume of water to be drained and the capacity of the transporting channel is translated into the equality of Q_{max} determined from Eq. (1.1), and Q_0 calculated from Eq. (1.3).

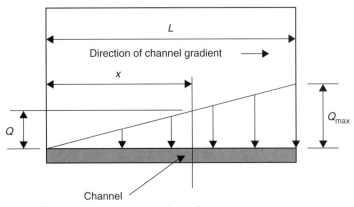

Figure 1.7 *Inflow to a linear drainage channel.*

The focus in the design of a traditional drainage system is on the spacing between the outlets, which is determined by the efficiency of the gully grating, or of the kerb inlet. The gully efficiency is defined as the ratio of the volume of flow entering the gully to the volume of flow approaching it. The same applies to the efficiency of the kerb inlet. Gully gratings are classified into various grades. For instance, a gully may either be of a heavy duty (D type) with efficiency varying from 84% to 99%, or of a medium duty (E type) with efficiency varying from 70% to 98% [1.2]. It is found that the main parameters on which the efficiency of a gully grating depends are the width of flow, and the longitudinal and side slopes of the channel estimated immediately upstream of the gully. A linear drainage channel is provided with one or more outfalls which are units specially built for the purpose of expelling water. The efficiency at which the water enters and leaves a linear drainage system is usually taken as 1·0, and the focus in design is on the capacity of the channel.

From the varied flow theory, it is found that the location of the maximum depth of flow in a drainage channel varies with the gradient of the channel. For instance, if the channel is laid level then the depth of flow is maximum at its upstream end. If a small gradient is introduced, then the location of the maximum depth moves downstream. A small increase in the gradient causes the deepest cross section of flow to move considerably downstream. Having reached the downstream end at a certain gradient, the maximum depth stays there at all steeper gradients.

For a channel of constant cross section, and laid at a uniform slope, the magnitude of the maximum depth increases with the length of the channel, a longer channel admitting more water. Since the depth of flow cannot exceed the available depth of the system, the capacity of the drainage system must necessarily be related to the length of the channel. Hence, before deciding upon the capacity of a linear drainage system, it is important to find both the location and the magnitude of the maximum depth for, although, the capacity is defined by the rate of discharge at the outlet, the limiting depth of flow may, or may not be at the outlet.

As a preliminary to the computation of varied flow in a drainage channel (to be discussed in later chapters), I consider the simple case of a rectangular area to be drained by means of a rectangular channel, and compare the results of the analysis using both the uniform flow and the varied flow theories. I assume that the channel is laid at a uniform gradient S_0, which may have a value ranging from 0 to 1/10. Let other data be as follows:

Width of channel $\qquad\qquad\qquad\qquad$ $B = 0.2\,\text{m}$
Depth of channel $\qquad\qquad\qquad\qquad$ $h = 0.24\,\text{m}$

The Manning's formula of the uniform flow theory (Chapter 3, Eq. (3.5)), gives the mean velocity of flow

$$U = \frac{R^{2/3}\sqrt{S_0}}{n} \tag{3.5}$$

in which R is the hydraulic radius, and n the coefficient of roughness. For the channel flowing at full capacity,

A = area of cross section of flow = area of cross section of the channel
$\quad = 0.2 \times 0.24 = 0.048\,\text{m}^2$
P = wetted perimeter = $0.2 + 0.48 = 0.68\,\text{m}$
R = hydraulic radius = $A/P = 0.0706\,\text{m}$

For $n = 0.011$, say, we obtain from Eq. (3.5)

$$U = \frac{0.0706^{2/3}}{0.011}\sqrt{S_0} = 15.527\sqrt{S_0}$$

The capacity of the channel Q_0 (in litres/second) is then given by

$$Q_0 = AU = 48.0 \times 15.527\sqrt{S_0} = 745.3\sqrt{S_0}$$

The values of Q_0 at various slopes calculated by this equation, which is the outcome of the *uniform flow* theory, and the corresponding values obtained by the application of the varied flow theory are shown in Table 1.1.

Table 1.1 *Comparison between channel capacities obtained from uniform and varied flow theories (X = distance of deepest cross section of flow from the upstream end)*

S_0	Uniform flow		Varied flow			
	U (m/s)	Q_0 (l/s)	L (m)	X (m)	U_0 (m/s)	Q_0 (l/s)
0	0	0	149	0	1·00	48·0
1/1000	0·491	23·57	216	148	1·14	57·4
1/500	0·694	33·33	265	217	1·22	58·6
1/200	1·10	52·70	378	357	1·37	65·8
1/100	1·55	74·53	520	520	1·49	71·5
1/50	2·20	105·40	745	745	2·14	102·7
1/20	3·47	166·65	1188	1188	3·42	164·2
1/10	4·91	235·68	1685	1685	4·87	233·8

Comparing these two sets of results, it is found that, for flat gradients, that is, up to about 1/100 in the example considered, the capacities calculated by the uniform flow theory are on the conservative side. At steeper slopes, the difference in the capacities is not very significant. However, the table also shows that, for a given slope, there is a maximum allowable length of the channel, that is, if the length of the channel exceeds this value then the depth of water will rise above the specified limit of 0·24 m. Therefore, these lengths must represent the theoretical maximum spacing between outlets.

1.3 Intensity of rainfall

Rainfall records suggest that, given the total amount of rainfall in an area, storms of shorter duration are more frequent than those of longer duration. This led to the evolution of the Bilham formula [1.3]

$$N_{10} = 1·25D(r + 0·1)^{-3·55} \tag{1.4}$$

where N_{10} = number of storms in 10 years, D = duration of storms in minutes, and r = total rainfall in inches.

By a simple transformation, Eq. (1.4) can be written as

$$I = \frac{1}{D}\left[14·14(ND)^{1/3·55} - 2·54\right] \tag{1.5}$$

where D = storm duration in hours, N = storm return period in years, and I = intensity of rainfall in mm/hr.

The Bilham formula is widely used in the United Kingdom, although preference is sometimes given to a formula depicting the local rainfall records, for instance, the Birmingham formula

$$I = \frac{40}{D + 20} \qquad 20 < D < 120 \text{ minutes}$$

However, in order to incorporate the local conditions in a general way, it has been necessary to modify the Bilham formula, the modified version is known as the Lloyd-Davies formula, or the 'rational' formula.

1.3.1   The Lloyd-Davies formula

The feature which distinguishes the Lloyd-Davies formula from the original Bilham formula is the replacement of the duration of rainfall by the *time of concentration*, and the application of the Bilham formula for each pipe length of the scheme, individually. This is to incorporate the evidence available from the records of intense storms that indicate the storm giving the highest discharge from a given catchment area occurs when the duration of the rainfall is equal to the time of concentration. The time of concentration is defined as the sum of the *entry time* (time taken by the water to flow across the surface) that is, from the farthest point of the area concerned to the point of entry to the channel, and the accumulated *time of flow* of water within the confines of the channel, that is, between the upstream and downstream ends of the channel. The normal range of the entry time is taken from 2 to 4 minutes, the larger value is applied to exceptionally large paved surfaces, and an accuracy of within 1/2 minute in the estimated entry time is considered adequate.

As mentioned above, a drainage scheme consists of a main channel and its several tributaries, and a tributary of the main channel may have its own tributaries. The main channel, which is usually the longest, and the tributaries are made up of various *lengths* of pipes separated by manholes (see Fig. 1.8). Since the volume of flow increases with the distance from the highest point of the area to be drained, heavier pipe sections are required as the flow progresses. It is, therefore, usual to find that different pipe lengths of a particular scheme have different times of flow and, hence, different times of concentration. Normally, pipes are selected from experience, assuming that they run just full, that is, without surcharge. This allows the time of flow to be calculated from a uniform flow formula. Alternatively, the velocity of flow can be obtained from the design tables [1.4] based on the Colebrook-White formula (see Chapter 4).

Each pipe length is identified by two numbers, say, m and n, separated by a dot. The first number m identifies the channel (main or tributary) to

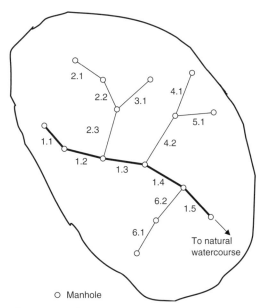

Figure 1.8 *Plan of a sewer system.*

which the length belongs, and the second number n identifies its location with respect to the most upstream manhole in the channel. Thus, assuming that both m and n start from 1, a length labelled as 2.3 means that it belongs to channel 2 in the scheme, and is third from the most upstream manhole in the channel (Fig. 1.8).

Denoting the time of concentration and the time of flow for a length $m.n$ by $T_{m.n}$ and $t_{m.n}$ respectively, and assuming that the entry time for all lengths is the same, we have

$$T_{m.n} = \sum_{i=1}^{n} t_{m.i} + \text{entry time}$$

that is,

$$T_{m.1} = t_{m.1} + \text{entry time} \tag{1.6}$$

and

$$T_{m.n} = T_{m.n-1} + t_{m.n} \tag{1.6a}$$

where $t_{m.i}$ is the time of flow in the length $m.i$.

The procedure based on the Lloyd-Davies formula, and adopted in the design of a storm sewer system is described in reference [1.5]. In the following example, the procedure is illustrated in greater detail. The velocities of flow are calculated from the Manning's formula (Eq. (3.5)).

Table 1.2 *Determination of time of concentration from the Lloyd-Davies formula (Example 1.1)*

1 Ref. length *m.n*	2 $L_{m.n}$ (m)	3 $d_{m.n}$ (mm)	4 $S_{0,m.n}$	5 $R_{m.n}$ (mm)	6 $U_{m.n}$ (m/s)	7 $t_{m.n}$ (min)	8 $T_{m.n}$ (min)
1.1	60	150	0·017	37·5	1·33	0·75	2·75
1.2	60	200	0·017	50·0	1·61	0·62	3·37
2.1	50	150	0·02	37·5	1·44	0·58	2·58
2.2	50	200	0·017	50·0	1·61	0·52	3·10
3.1	50	150	0·025	37·5	1·61	0·52	2·52
2.3	60	250	0·025	50·0	2·26	0·44	3·54
1.3	80	300	0·03	75·0	2·80	0·48	3·85
4.1	60	150	0·025	37·5	1·61	0·62	2·62
5.1	60	150	0·017	37·5	1·33	0·75	2·75
4.2	60	250	0·02	62·5	2·02	0·49	3·11
1.4	50	350	0·03	87·5	3·10	0·27	4·12
6.1	50	150	0·027	37·5	1·67	0·50	2·50
6.2	50	200	0·02	50·0	1·74	0·48	2·98
1.5	50	400	0·025	100·0	3·10	0·27	4·39

Example 1.1: The plan of a sewer system consisting of several lengths of circular pipes is shown in Fig. 1.8. If the estimated entry time is 2 minutes, and the coefficient of roughness $n = 0·011$, determine the times of concentration for all lengths involved.

Solution: Table 1.2, which represents the solution, consists of the following columns

> *Column 1*   pipe reference number *m.n*.
> *Column 2* $L_{m.n}$ = length of the pipe *m.n*.
> *Column 3* $d_{m.n}$ = assumed diameter of the pipe *m.n*.
> *Column 4* $S_{0,m.n}$ = longitudinal gradient of the pipe *m.n*.
> *Column 5* $R_{m.n}$ = hydraulic radius of the pipe *m.n*.
>   Assuming that the pipe runs full, $R_{m.n} = d_{m.n}/4$
> *Column 6* $U_{m.n}$ = mean velocity of flow in the pipe *m.n*.

$$U_{m.n} = \frac{(R_{m.n})^{2/3}\sqrt{S_{0,m.n}}}{n}$$

$$U_{1.1} = \frac{(0·0375)^{2/3}\sqrt{0·017}}{0·011} = 1·33 \text{ m/s, and so forth.}$$

Column 7 $t_{m.n}$ = time of flow in the pipe $m.n = L_{m.n}/U_{m.n}$

$$t_{1.1} = \frac{60}{1\cdot33 \times 60} = 0\cdot75 \text{ minutes, and so forth.}$$

Column 8 $T_{m.n}$ = time of concentration in pipe $m.n$.
From Eq. (1.6), $T_{1.1} = t_{1.1} + 2\cdot0 = 2\cdot75$ minutes.
From Eq. (1.6a), $T_{1.2} = T_{1.1} + t_{1.2} = 2\cdot75 + 0\cdot62 = 3\cdot37$ minutes, and so forth.

The next step in runoff calculations is to find the intensity of rainfall for each length of the sewer system. This is done by substituting the respective times of concentration for the duration of rainfall in the Bilham formula. The surface area $A_{s,m.n}$ contributing to the runoff drained by the length $m.n$ is determined as follows:

$$A_{s,m.n} = A_{s,m.n-1} + a_{s,m.n} + A^{*}_{s,m.n} \tag{1.7}$$

$$A_{s,m.1} = a_{s,m.1} \tag{1.7a}$$

where

$\quad a_{s,m.n}$ = area to be drained exclusively by the length $m.n$
$A_{s,m.n-1}$ = cumulative surface area drained by all lengths of the pipe m, upstream of $m.n$
$A^{*}_{s,m.n}$ = cumulative surface area drained by all other pipes discharging into the manhole between the pipes $m.n - 1$ and $m.n$.

The total runoff in each individual length is then obtained from Eq. (1.1). This is compared with the capacity of the channel length obtained from Eq. (1.3). If the capacity of the channel is found to be less than the runoff then the pipe diameter has to be revised.

Example 1.2: The area to be drained by each pipe length of the sewer system shown in Fig. 1.8 is given in column 4 of Table 1.3. For a storm frequency of 1 year, determine the runoff (litres per second) for each channel length, and check the value against the flow capacity of each pipe.

Solution: The solution is presented in Table 1.3 which contains the following columns:

Column 1   pipe reference number $m.n$.
Column 2 $D_{m.n}$ = duration of rainfall for the pipe $m.n = T_{m.n}$
Column 3 $I_{m.n}$ = intensity of rainfall for the pipe $m.n$ obtained from Eq. (1.5).

Table 1.3 *Determination of intensity of rainfall and maximum discharge from the Lloyd-Davies formula (Example 1.1)*

1 Ref. length $m.n$	2 $D_{m.n}$ (min)	3 $I_{m.n}$ (mm/hr)	4 $a_{s,m.n}$ (m²)	5 $A_{s,m.n}$ (m²)	6 $Q_{max,m.n}$ (l/s)	7 $A_{m.n}$ (m²) × 1000	8 $Q_{0,m.n}$ (l/s)
1.1	2·75	74	1000	1000	20·56	17·67	23·50
1.2	3·37	66	800	1800	33·50	31·42	50·58
2.1	2·58	76	1200	1200	25·33	17·67	25·44
2.2	3·10	69	600	1800	35·00	31·42	50·58
3.1	2·52	77	1200	1200	25·67	17·67	28·45
2.3	3·54	64	1200	4200	75·83	49·09	61·26*
1.3	3·85	62	1600	7600	130·89	70·69	197·92
4.1	2·62	75	1200	1200	25·33	17·67	28·45
5.1	2·75	73	1000	1000	20·55	17·67	23·50
4.2	3·11	69	800	3000	58·33	49·09	54·66*
1.4	4·12	59	1200	11 800	196·67	96·21	298·25
6.1	2·50	77	1200	1200	26·00	17·67	29·51
6.2	2·98	70	1400	2600	51·28	31·42	54·67
1.5	4·39	57	1500	15 900	256·17	125·66	389·56

* See text.

Hence, for $N = 1$,

$$I_{m.n} = \frac{1}{D_{m.n}}\left[14\cdot14(D_{m.n})^{1/3\cdot55} - 2\cdot54\right]$$

Column 4 $a_{s,m.n}$ = surface area drained, exclusively, by the pipe $m.n$.
Column 5 $A_{s,m.n}$ = cumulative surface area drained by the pipe $m.n$.
For instance, from Eqs (1.7), $A_{s,1.1} = a_{s,1.1} = 1000\,\text{m}^2$
$A_{s,1.2} = A_{s,1.1} + a_{s,1.2} = 1000 + 800 = 1800\,\text{m}^2$
$A^*_{s,1.3} = A_{s,2.3} = 3000\,\text{m}^2$
Therefore, $A_{s,1.3} = A_{s,1.2} + a_{s,1.3} + A^*_{s,1.3} = 1800 + 1600 + 3000$
$= 6400\,\text{m}^2$
It can be verified that the last entry in column 5 is the sum of all entries in column 4.
Column 6 $Q_{max,m.n}$ = runoff carried by pipe $m.n$.
Taking $C_r = 1\cdot0$, we obtain from Eq. (1.1)

$$Q_{max,1.0} = \frac{74 \times 1000}{3600} = 20\cdot56\,\text{l/s, and so forth.}$$

Column 7 $A_{m.n}$ = area of cross section of the pipe $m.n = \pi d^2_{m.n}/4$

Column 8 $Q_{0,m.n}$ = flow capacity of the pipe $m.n = U_{m.n} A_{m.n}$
            where $U_{m.n}$ is taken from column 6 of Table 1.2.

It can be seen from Table 1.3 that pipes labelled 2.3 and 4.2 (denoted by asterisk in column 8) have insufficient capacity, thus requiring their diameters to be revised. All other pipe lengths are capable of carrying the volume of runoff.

1.3.2   The Wallingford procedure

The Wallingford procedure [1.6] is a modified form of the Lloyd-Davies formula. It calculates the peak discharge from the formula

$$Q_{max} = \frac{C_r IA_s}{0\cdot36} = 2\cdot78 C_r IA_s \tag{1.8}$$

in which A_s is in hectares (1 hectare = 10^4 m^2). This formula is applicable to urban areas of up to 150 ha, with uniformly distributed impervious surfaces, and to rainfall of duration in excess of 5 minutes. The runoff coefficient C_r is split into the volumetric runoff coefficient C_{rv} and the routing coefficient C_{rr}:

$$C_r = C_{rv} C_{rr} \tag{1.9}$$

The volumetric coefficient C_{rv} depends upon the permeability of the surface. Its value ranges from about $0\cdot6$ for areas made up of rapidly draining soils to about $0\cdot9$ for heavy soils, or paved surfaces. An average value of $0\cdot75$ is therefore recommended. The routing coefficient C_{rr} depends upon the shape of the *time-area diagram* [1.7], and on the variation of rainfall with the time of concentration. The recommended value for C_{rr} is $1\cdot3$, which leads to the usual practice of taking $C_r = 1\cdot0$.

As was done in the application of the Lloyd-Davies formula, the intensity of rainfall is calculated on the basis of the time of concentration, but by a procedure recommended by the Meteorological Office [1.8]. The central parameter involved in this procedure is M_{T-D}, the depth of flow associated with the specified values of the return period T and the duration of storm D. The return time is specified by the drainage authority using the procedure, and the duration of storm is calculated by the procedure illustrated in Example 1.2.

For a given region, the basic data available are as follows:

(a) M_{5-60}, the depth of rainfall for $T = 5$ years, and $D = 60$ minutes. The value is obtained from a map of the United Kingdom (Fig. 1.9), showing contours of various depths of rainfall.

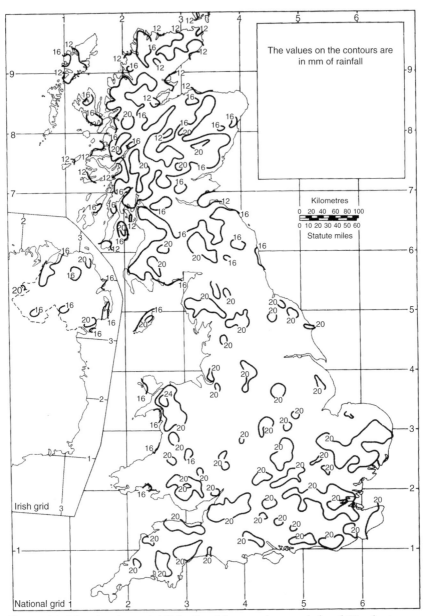

Figure 1.9 *Map showing rainfall depths of 5-year return period and 60-minute duration (M$_{5-60}$) in the United Kingdom.*

(b) The conversion factor r defined by

$$r = \frac{M_{5-2\,day}}{M_{5-60\,min}} \tag{1.10}$$

Its value is obtained also from a map of the United Kingdom (Fig. 1.10).
(c) The ratio z_1 is defined by the equation

$$z_1 = \frac{M_{5-D}}{M_{5-60\,min}} \tag{1.11}$$

Corresponding to the value of r determined in (b), and the specified D, the value of z_1 is read from a graph shown in Figs 1.11(a) and 1.11(b).
(d) The parameter z_2, defined by the equation

$$z_2 = \frac{M_{T-D}}{M_{5-D\,min}} \tag{1.12}$$

The value of z_2 is obtained from Tables 1.4(a) and 1.4(b).
(e) The area reduction factor (A_{RF}), which depends on the extent of the area contributing to flow, and the duration of rainfall. Its value is taken from the graph shown in Fig. 1.12.

Finally, the intensity of rainfall is then given by

$$I = \frac{M_{T-D}}{D} \tag{1.13}$$

The following example illustrates the procedure.

Example 1.3: For a certain location in England, $M_{5-60\,min} = 20\,mm$, and $r = 42 \cdot 0\%$. Determine the intensity of rainfall over an area of $2\,km^2$ for $T = 2$ years, and $D = 30$ minutes.

Solution: For $r = 0 \cdot 42$ and $D = 30$ minutes, we obtain from Fig. 1.11(b)

$$z_1 = 0 \cdot 8$$

Hence, from Eq. (1.11), the depth of rainfall of the specified duration of $D = 30$ minutes is

$$M_{5-30\,min} = 0 \cdot 8(M_{5-60\,min}) = 0 \cdot 8 \times 20 = 16 \cdot 0\,mm$$

From Table 1.4

$$z_2 = 0 \cdot 80$$

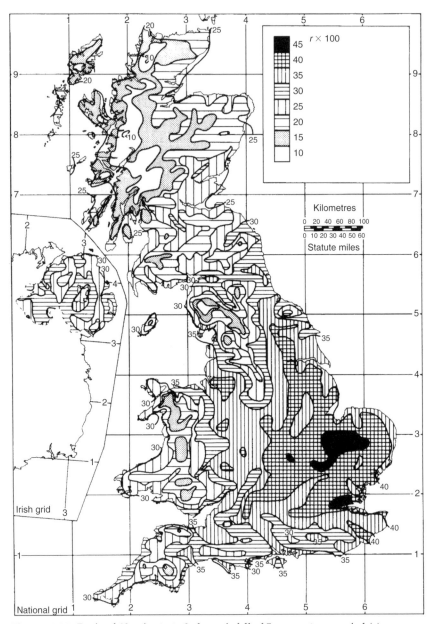

Figure 1.10 *Ratio of 60-minute to 2-day rainfall of 5-year return period* (r).

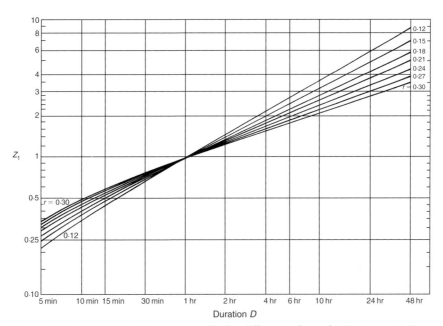

Figure 1.11(a) *Relation between z_1 and D for different values of r ($0 \cdot 12 \leqslant r \leqslant 0 \cdot 3$).*

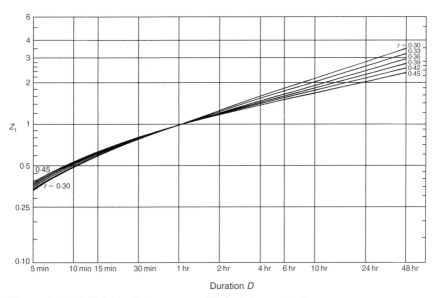

Figure 1.11(b) *Relation between z_1 and D for $0 \cdot 3 \leqslant r \leqslant 0 \cdot 45$.*

Table 1.4(a) *Relationship between rainfall of arbitrary return period* T *and rainfall of return period of 5 years (England and Wales)*

M_5 (mm)	Ratio (z_2) of M_T to M_5 rainfalls								
	M_1	M_2	M_3	M_4	M_5	M_{10}	M_{20}	M_{50}	M_{100}
5	0·62	0·79	0·89	0·97	1·02	1·19	1·36	1·56	1·79
10	0·61	0·79	0·90	0·97	1·03	1·22	1·41	1·65	1·91
15	0·62	0·80	0·90	0·97	1·03	1·24	1·44	1·70	1·99
20	0·64	0·80	0·90	0·97	1·03	1·24	1·45	1·73	2·03
25	0·66	0·82	0·91	0·97	1·03	1·24	1·44	1·72	2·01
30	0·68	0·83	0·91	0·97	1·03	1·22	1·42	1·70	1·97
40	0·70	0·84	0·92	0·97	1·02	1·19	1·38	1·64	1·89
50	0·72	0·85	0·93	0·98	1·02	1·17	1·34	1·58	1·81
75	0·76	0·87	0·93	0·98	1·02	1·14	1·44	1·47	1·64
100	0·78	0·88	0·94	0·98	1·02	1·13	1·42	1·40	1·54
150	0·78	0·88	0·94	0·98	1·01	1·12	1·21	1·33	1·45
200	0·78	0·88	0·94	0·98	1·01	1·11	1·19	1·30	1·40

Table 1.4(b) *Relationship between rainfall of arbitrary return period* T *and rainfall of return period of 5 years (Scotland and Northern Ireland)*

M_5 (mm)	Ratio (z_2) of M_T to M_5 rainfalls								
	M_1	M_2	M_3	M_4	M_5	M_{10}	M_{20}	M_{50}	M_{100}
5	0·67	0·82	0·91	0·98	1·02	1·17	1·35	1·62	1·86
10	0·68	0·82	0·91	0·98	1·03	1·19	1·39	1·69	1·97
15	0·69	0·83	0·91	0·97	1·03	1·20	1·39	1·70	1·98
20	0·70	0·84	0·92	0·97	1·02	1·19	1·39	1·66	1·93
25	0·71	0·84	0·92	0·98	1·02	1·18	1·37	1·64	1·89
30	0·72	0·85	0·92	0·98	1·02	1·18	1·36	1·61	1·85
40	0·74	0·86	0·93	0·98	1·02	1·17	1·34	1·56	1·77
50	0·75	0·87	0·93	0·98	1·02	1·16	1·30	1·52	1·72
75	0·77	0·88	0·94	0·98	1·02	1·14	1·27	1·45	1·62
100	0·78	0·88	0·94	0·98	1·02	1·13	1·24	1·40	1·54
150	0·79	0·89	0·94	0·98	1·02	1·11	1·20	1·33	1·45
200	0·80	0·89	0·95	0·99	1·01	1·10	1·18	1·30	1·40

When this value is substituted in Eq. (1.12), the result is the depth of rainfall of the specified duration of $D = 30$ minutes and return period of 2 years. That is,

$$M_{2-30\,\text{min}} = 0·80 \times 16·0 = 12·8 \text{ mm}$$

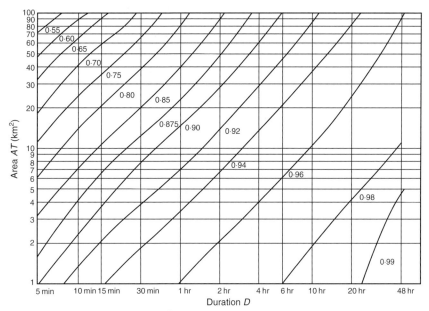

Figure 1.12 *Area reduction factor* A_{RF} *related to area and duration of rainfall.*

For $D = 30$ minutes, and $2\,\text{km}^2$ as the area to be drained, the area reduction factor is about $0{\cdot}94$, therefore

$$M_{2-30\,\text{min}} = 0{\cdot}94 \times 12{\cdot}8 = 12{\cdot}03\,\text{mm}$$

The average intensity of rainfall is then obtained from Eq. (1.13):

$$I = \frac{12{\cdot}03}{(30/60)} = 24{\cdot}1\,\text{mm/hr}$$

1.3.3 The formula for intensity of rainfall applied to gully spacing

The time of concentration used in the design of gully spacing is usually less than 5 minutes, which is out of the range of application of the Wallingford procedure. Hence, in such situations, an alternative formula recommended by the Highway Agency is to be used (see Chapter 9).

References

[1.1] SALTER R.G., *Highway Design and Construction*, 2nd edn, Macmillan Education, London, 1988.

[1.2] RUSSAM K.H., *The Hydraulic Efficiency and Spacing of British Standard Road Gullies*, Road Research Laboratory report LR 277, 1969.

[1.3] BILHAM E.G.J., *The Classification of Heavy Falls of Rain in Short Periods*, British Rainfall 1935, HMSO, London, 1936, 262–280.

[1.4] WALLINGFORD H.R. and BARR D.I.H., *Tables for the Hydraulic Design of Pipes, Sewers and Channels*, 7th edn, Vol. II, Thomas Telford, London, 1998.

[1.5] *A Guide for Engineers to the Design of Storm Sewer Systems*, Road Note 35, Road Research Laboratory, 1963.

[1.6] *Design and Analysis of Urban Storm Drainage, The Wallingford Procedure*, Vol. 4, The Modified Rational Method, Hydraulic Research, Wallingford, 1981.

[1.7] WHITE J.B., *Design of Sewers and Sewage Treatment Works*, Edward Arnold, London, 1970, ch. 4.

[1.8] *Rainfall Memorandum No. 4*, Meteorological Office, London, 1977.

2

Basic properties of channel flow

The equations of flow in an open channel relate the geometric parameters of the cross section, such as wetted perimeter and hydraulic depth, with the flow parameters, such as velocity and momentum, through laws of physics and experimental evidence. After a brief introduction of the types of flow encountered in practice, this chapter contains the derivation of geometric parameters of elementary shapes commonly used in drainage channels. This has been found necessary, so that they could be referred to when advancing the discussion through later chapters. Also included in the chapter is the derivation of forces and energies that constitute the flow mechanism. A section on the Froude and Reynolds numbers is also included. Since the flow may, or may not, occupy the whole cross section of the channel, in this text the term 'cross section' means the cross section of the flow, and not necessarily that of the channel.

2.1 Types of flow in open channels

The flow in a drainage channel is essentially a free-surface flow, which means that the only external force acting on a volume of flow is atmospheric. For this reason, the properties of flow encountered in drainage channels, in general, lie in the domain of open channel hydraulics. However, before focusing on the specialized topic of flow in drainage channels and, in particular, linear drainage channels, it is necessary to introduce briefly the types of flow that occur in these channels.

The simplest type of flow in a channel is the *uniform flow,* of which the velocity, depth and area of cross section are constant over the entire length of the channel. However, in real life, this type of flow rarely occurs because natural watercourses are inherently irregular, and there is a constant increase in the volume of flow in man-made drainage channels, introducing variability to the flow. It is imperative, therefore, to treat the flow as *non-uniform.* We also observe that the variation of flow in a normal drainage channel is gradual which is in contrast with the rapid flow, such as the flow over a spillway. In a *gradually varied flow*, the pressure distribution over the cross section of flow is hydrostatic, extending the validity of the relationship between the coefficient of roughness and the mean velocity of flow, initially developed for the uniform flow, to varied flow. In a *rapidly varied flow*, because of the sharpness and, possibly, sudden changes of curvature of the streamlines, the pressure distribution cannot be hydrostatic. Since the subject matter presented here concerns only drainage systems, one must assume that the volume of flow not only increases linearly but also gradually. Such flows are studied under the broad heading of *spatially varied flow*, although the variation of flow is restricted to only along the length of the channel. Furthermore, since the cross section of a drainage channel is generally constant, the variation of the flow is reflected only in the variation of the depth of flow.

The flow may be *unsteady* if the rate of flow varies with time, or *steady* if it does not. The flow in drainage channels is taken as steady. Examples of unsteady flow are tidal flows, flood waves and flows in the vicinity of control structures such as sluice gates. These topics are out of the scope of this book, but can be found in many text books on channel flow (see, for instance, references [2.1, 2.2, 2.3]).

Flows are also classified according to the ratios of inertial force to gravitational and viscous forces described in section 2.12. When the ratio of the inertial force to the gravitational force is less than 1, the flow is described as *sub-critical (tranquil)*, *super-critical (shooting)* if it exceeds 1. The square root of this ratio is called the *Froude number*, and is denoted by F. The flow is said to be critical when the Froude number is unity. Because of the absence of inertial force, the uniform flow is always sub-critical. Super-critical flow may occur when the flow in a channel is of the varied type, and the slope is steep. Critical flow in open channels is particularly important as it occurs at *controls* and, frequently, at the outfalls. It can be demonstrated that critical flow is an unstable condition of flow.

The ratio of the inertial force to the viscous force, acting on a unit volume, is called the *Reynolds number*, and is denoted by R. It is generally accepted that when this ratio does not exceed 2000 the flow is *laminar*, and *turbulent* if it does. The laminar flow is characterized by a slow and orderly movement of fluid particles in layers (laminae), one layer sliding over the adjacent layer, allowing the viscous force to dominate the flow. In turbulent flow, the movement of fluid particles is irregular with a continuous exchange of momentum between fluid molecules. This phenomenon is called *mixing* of flow. As a result, the velocity distribution over the cross section is more uniform in turbulent flow than in laminar flow. The main body of flow in an open channel is almost always turbulent.

2.2 Hydraulic properties, channel gradient

All hydraulic properties used in the design of a channel are associated with the cross section, the exception being the gradient, which is specified in the longitudinal direction. The properties include the geometric parameters such as the depth, and the area of cross section, and the flow parameters such as the velocity and the rate of discharge. The constitutive equations of flow in an open channel combine the hydraulic properties according to the laws of physics. While the geometric parameters depend upon the shape of the cross section, the flow parameters are indicative of the flow actually taking place. The flow parameter at the centre of open-channel hydraulics is the mean velocity of flow. In order to understand the mechanism of flow from a theoretical standpoint, it is necessary to consider also such parameters as momentum and energy associated with the flow.

The gradient of the channel bed, also known as the *channel gradient* or the *bed slope* S_0 (see Fig. 2.1), is to generate sufficient gravitational force to take the flow to its intended destination, by counterbalancing any resistance. The gradient is also required to produce sufficient velocity so that silting of the channel is prevented. Excessive bed slopes should be avoided as they might cause erosion of the channel surface. In equation form, the bed slope is defined as

$$S_0 = \lim_{\delta x \to 0} \frac{\delta z}{\delta x} = -\frac{dz}{dx} \tag{2.1}$$

where x is measured along the length of the channel (positive in the downstream direction) and z is the altitude of the point x measured from arbitrary horizontal datum. The negative sign indicates a downward slope (decreasing z with increasing x).

The two special values of bed slopes, which depend on the cross section of the flow, are the *normal slope* and the *critical slope*. These are discussed later. In a uniform flow situation, the bed slope is equal to the loss of energy

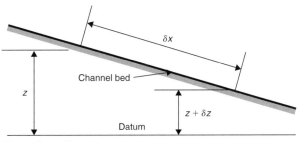

Figure 2.1 *Channel gradient.*

per unit weight of water due to friction, and is called the *friction slope* (see section 3.3). Since the bed slopes are usually much less than 1, it is common not to distinguish between the sine and the tangent of the angle that the channel bed makes with the horizontal.

It is generally assumed that the bed slope remains constant over the length of the channel, although there have been attempts to incorporate the variation of slope from one segment of length to another [2.4]. However, this situation has been excluded from the treatment of channel flow presented here. In general, the bed slope depends on the topography of the area.

2.3   Geometric parameters

To begin, the definitions of the principal geometric parameters involved in the equations of channel flow are:

Depth of flow (*y*)
Area of cross section (*A*)
Top width (*T*)
Wetted perimeter (*P*)
Hydraulic depth (*D*)
Hydraulic radius (*R*)

The *depth of flow y* is measured vertically from the channel bed. In the study of varied flow, the depth of flow is the most important parameter, for it is the principal unknown in the equation of motion. To ensure that, at any point, the depth of flow does not exceed the available depth of the channel, it is often required to compute the *flow profile* showing the depth of flow along the entire length of the channel. The computation of the flow profile also leads to the determination of the capacity and the maximum length of the channel that can be allowed for a specified bed slope.

The *area of cross section* of flow *A* is defined as the area occupied by the fluid normal to the direction of flow. The cross-sectional area remains constant over the length of the channel if the flow is uniform, but varies if the flow is non-uniform.

The *top width T* is the width of the cross section of flow at the free surface. It can be shown that, when the area of cross section is expressed as an explicit function of *y*, the top width satisfies the equation

$$\frac{dA}{dy} = T \tag{2.2}$$

This relationship holds for all shapes of channel cross sections.

The *wetted perimeter* P is the perimeter of that part of the cross section of the channel that is in contact with the fluid. Since the shear stress due to the surface roughness is the major source of resistance to flow, it is desirable that the cross section should have a minimum wetted perimeter. A rectangular channel with $B = 2y$, and a trapezoidal channel with the cross section in the shape of half of a regular hexagon are examples of channels which satisfy this requirement (see Examples 2.1 and 2.2). It can be verified that, for a given cross sectional area, a semicircular channel provides a minimum wetted perimeter. However, the condition of the wetted perimeter being minimum does not always control the selection of a drainage system for, from the manufacturer's point of view, a particular shape of the channel may sometimes have greater appeal.

The *hydraulic depth D* is the ratio of the area of cross section to the top width:

$$D = \frac{A}{T} \qquad (2.3)$$

In a rectangular channel, the hydraulic depth and the depth of flow are identical. The hydraulic depth of a channel is the *characteristic length* in the expression for the Froude number, *F*, a non-dimensional parameter, the magnitude of which identifies the flow as sub-critical or super-critical (see Chapter 6).

The *hydraulic radius R* is the ratio of the area of cross section of flow to the wetted perimeter:

$$R = \frac{A}{P} \qquad (2.4)$$

The hydraulic radius is the *characteristic length* in the expression for the Reynolds number, *R*, which identifies the flow as laminar or turbulent.

2.4 Geometric parameters, elementary shapes

Channel sections especially manufactured for the disposal of surface water do not have to conform to simple geometric shapes such as rectangular or trapezoidal, and different manufacturers use different geometrical shapes. However, for the sake of simplicity in the development of the theoretical analysis, it is necessary to consider only elementary geometrical shapes. This section contains the derivation of the geometric parameters of the following basic shapes that are commonly used in open channels.

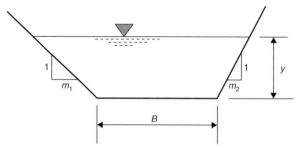

Figure 2.2 *Trapezoidal channel.*

2.4.1 Trapezoidal section

The parameters necessary to define the cross section of flow in a trapezoidal channel, shown in Fig. 2.2, are the bottom width B, the side slopes m_1 and m_2, and the depth y. The corresponding hydraulic properties are

$$A = \left[B + \frac{1}{2}(m_1 + m_2)y \right] y \tag{2.5a}$$

$$T = B + (m_1 + m_2)y \tag{2.5b}$$

$$P = B + \left(\sqrt{1 + m_1^2} + \sqrt{1 + m_2^2} \right) y \tag{2.5c}$$

$$D = \frac{\left[B + (1/2)(m_1 + m_2)y \right] y}{B + (m_1 + m_2)y} \tag{2.5d}$$

$$R = \frac{\left[B + (1/2)(m_1 + m_2)y \right] y}{B + \left(\sqrt{1 + m_1^2} + \sqrt{1 + m_2^2} \right) y} \tag{2.5e}$$

2.4.2 Triangular section

The cross section of a triangular channel can be defined by the depth of flow and the side slopes of the channel. Hence, the hydraulic properties of a triangular channel can be derived from those of a trapezoidal channel by setting $B = 0$. Hence

$$A = \frac{1}{2}(m_1 + m_2)y^2 \tag{2.6a}$$

$$T = (m_1 + m_2)y \tag{2.6b}$$

$$P = \left(\sqrt{1 + m_1^2} + \sqrt{1 + m_2^2}\right)y \tag{2.6c}$$

$$D = \frac{1}{2}y \tag{2.6d}$$

$$R = \frac{(1/2)(m_1 + m_2)}{\sqrt{1 + m_1^2} + \sqrt{1 + m_2^2}}y \tag{2.6e}$$

2.4.3   Rectangular section

The cross section of flow in a rectangular channel is defined by the width B of the channel, and the depth of flow y. Hence, the hydraulic properties of a rectangular channel can also be derived from those of the trapezoidal channel, this time by setting the side slopes to zero. Thus, for a rectangular channel:

$$A = By \tag{2.7a}$$

$$T = B \tag{2.7b}$$

$$P = B + 2y \tag{2.7c}$$

$$D = y \tag{2.7d}$$

$$R = \frac{By}{B + 2y} \tag{2.7e}$$

2.4.4   Circular section

A circular channel is defined by the diameter d of the cross section, and it is convenient to express the hydraulic properties of the cross section of the flow in terms of d and θ, the latter being half of the angle subtended by the wetted perimeter (Fig. 2.3).

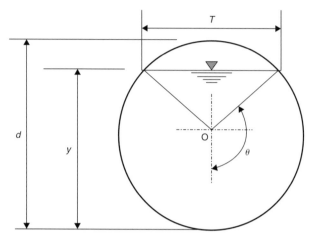

Figure 2.3 *Cross section of a circular pipe.*

From Fig. 2.3, we obtain

$$y = \frac{1}{2}(1 - \cos \theta)d \tag{2.8a}$$

$$A = \frac{1}{4}(\theta - \sin \theta \cos \theta)d^2 \tag{2.8b}$$

$$T = (\sin \theta)d \tag{2.8c}$$

$$P = \theta d \tag{2.8d}$$

$$D = \frac{A}{T} = \frac{1}{4}\left[\frac{1}{\sin \theta}(\theta - \sin \theta \cos \theta)\right]d \tag{2.8e}$$

$$R = \frac{A}{P} = \frac{1}{4}\left(1 - \frac{1}{\theta}\sin \theta \cos \theta\right)d \tag{2.8f}$$

For a full-running circular pipe $R = d/4$.

2.4.5 Parabolic section

A parabolic cross section of flow, shown in Fig. 2.4, is defined by the top width T and the water depth y. At any point within the cross section, the depth y_1, and the width $2x_1$, satisfy the equation

$$x_1^2 = \frac{T^2}{4y}y_1 \tag{2.9}$$

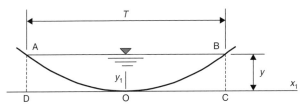

Figure 2.4 *Cross section of a parabolic channel.*

The hydraulic properties of the cross section are as follows:

$$A = \frac{2}{3}(\text{area of rectangle ABCD}) = \frac{2}{3}Ty \qquad (2.10)$$

The wetted perimeter is given by

$$P = 2\int_0^{T/2} \sqrt{1 + \left(\frac{dy_1}{dx_1}\right)^2}\, dx_1 = 2\int_0^{T/2} \sqrt{1 + \left(\frac{8y}{T}\right)^2}\, x_1^2 dx_1$$

from which, using the notation

$$\phi = \frac{2x_1}{T} \qquad \psi = \frac{4y}{T}$$

we obtain

$$P = T\int_0^1 \sqrt{1 + \psi^2\phi^2}\, d\phi$$

$$= \psi T \int_0^1 \sqrt{\frac{1}{\psi^2} + \phi^2}\, d\phi$$

$$= \frac{\psi T}{2}\left[\phi\sqrt{\frac{1}{\psi^2} + \phi^2} + \frac{1}{\psi^2}\sinh^{-1}(\psi\phi)\right]_0^1$$

$$= \frac{\psi T}{2}\left[\sqrt{\frac{1}{\psi^2} + 1} + \frac{1}{\psi^2}\sinh^{-1}\psi\right]$$

$$= \frac{\psi T}{2}\left[\sqrt{\frac{1}{\psi^2} + 1} + \frac{1}{\psi^2}\ln\left(\psi + \sqrt{1 + \psi^2}\right)\right]$$

that is,

$$P = \frac{T}{2}\left[\sqrt{1 + \psi^2} + \frac{1}{\psi} ln\left(\psi + \sqrt{1 + \psi^2} \right) \right] \tag{2.11a}$$

For a channel which is sufficiently shallow so that

$$\psi \ll 1 \quad \text{or} \quad T \gg 4y,$$

a simplified formula for P can be obtained by expanding the right-hand side of the above equation in powers of ψ, and ignoring terms containing higher powers of ψ than 2. Thus

$$\sqrt{1 + \psi^2} \approx 1 + \frac{1}{2}\psi^2$$

and

$$\frac{1}{\psi} ln\left(\psi + \sqrt{1 + \psi^2} \right) \approx \frac{1}{\psi} ln\left(1 + \psi + \frac{1}{2}\psi^2 \right)$$

$$\approx \frac{1}{\psi}\left[\psi + \frac{1}{2}\psi^2 - \frac{\left(\psi + (1/2)\psi^2 \right)^2}{2} + \frac{\left(\psi + (1/2)\psi^2 \right)^3}{3} \right]$$

$$\approx \frac{1}{\psi}\left(\psi + \frac{1}{2}\psi^2 - \frac{1}{2}\psi^2 - \frac{1}{2}\psi^3 + \frac{1}{3}\psi^3 \right)$$

that is,

$$\frac{1}{\psi} ln\left(\psi + \sqrt{1 + \psi^2} \right) \approx 1 - \frac{1}{6}\psi^2$$

With these simplifications, we obtain

$$P = \frac{T}{2}\left(2 + \frac{1}{3}\psi^2 \right) = T + \frac{1}{6}T\left(\frac{16y^2}{T^2} \right)$$

that is,

$$P = T + \frac{8}{3}\frac{y^2}{T} \tag{2.11b}$$

$$D = \frac{A}{T} = \frac{2}{3}y \qquad (2.11c)$$

Corresponding to the approximate expression for P, we have

$$R = \frac{(2/3)Ty}{T\left(1 + (8/3)(y^2/T^2)\right)} = \frac{2yT^2}{3T^2 + 8y^2} \qquad (2.11d)$$

2.5 Best hydraulic section, the conveyance

The discharge-carrying capacity of a channel, carrying a uniform flow, is sometimes referred to as the *conveyance, K,* which, for the best hydraulic section must be maximum. The usual expression for K is

$$K = CAR^m \qquad (2.12)$$

where C is a coefficient of friction, and m is an exponent in the uniform flow formula used for calculating the velocity of flow (section 3.1). For instance, if the Chezy formula is used then, from Eq. (3.5)

$$C = \frac{1}{n}R^{-1/6}$$

and

$$m = \frac{1}{2} \qquad (Eq. (3.3))$$

giving

$$K = \frac{1}{n}AR^{2/3} \qquad (2.13)$$

From this equation, it is evident that, given the cross-sectional area, the conveyance of a channel increases with the increase in the hydraulic radius, that is, decrease in the wetted perimeter. This leads to the notion of the *best hydraulic section.*

In most cases of open channel flows, K increases with the depth of flow, leaving the issue of the best hydraulic section to be settled by minimizing the wetted perimeter. For, if K_0 is the maximum conveyance for a specified area A of cross section of flow, and P_0 is the corresponding wetted perimeter, then

$$\frac{K}{K_0} = \left(\frac{P_0}{P}\right)^{2/3} \qquad (2.14)$$

In the case of a closed conduit, such as a circular pipe, the question is of finding the depth of flow at which $AR^{2/3}$ is maximum.

2.5.1 Best rectangular section

For a rectangular channel

$$A = By$$

$$P = B + 2y = \frac{A}{y} + 2y$$

By setting

$$\frac{dP}{dy} = 0$$

we obtain

$$A = 2y^2$$

that is,

$$B = 2y$$

Hence, given the area of cross section of a rectangular channel, the wetted perimeter is minimum when the width of the channel is twice the depth of flow, and it can be verified that, for the ratio $\alpha = y/B$

$$\frac{K}{K_0} = \left(\frac{2\sqrt{2\alpha}}{1 + 2\alpha} \right)^{2/3} \tag{2.15}$$

2.5.2 Best trapezoidal section

From the relationships

$$A = \left[B + \frac{1}{2}(m_1 + m_2)y \right] y \tag{2.5a}$$

and

$$P = B + \left(\sqrt{1 + m_1^2} + \sqrt{1 + m_2^2} \right) y \tag{2.5c}$$

we obtain by eliminating B

$$Py = A + \left(\sqrt{1 + m_1^2} + \sqrt{1 + m_2^2} \right) y^2 - \frac{1}{2}(m_1 + m_2)y^2 \tag{i}$$

Setting

$$\frac{\partial P}{\partial m_1} = 0 \qquad \frac{\partial P}{\partial m_2} = 0 \qquad \frac{\partial P}{\partial y} = 0$$

the first two equations gives

$$m_1 = m_2 = \frac{1}{\sqrt{3}} \tag{ii}$$

When this result is used in the third equation, we obtain

$$P = 2\sqrt{3y}$$

that is,

$$y = \frac{P}{2\sqrt{3}} \tag{iii}$$

The substitution of Eqs (ii) and (iii), above, into Eq. (2.5c) results in

$$B = \frac{1}{3}P$$

which means that all three sides of the trapezium are equal. Hence, given the area of cross section of a trapezoidal channel, the wetted perimeter is minimum when the trapezium is made up of three sides of a regular hexagon.

2.5.3 Optimum depth of flow in a circular pipe

From Eqs (2.8b) and (2.8f), we obtain

$$AR^{2/3} = \frac{A^{5/3}}{P^{2/3}} = \frac{\left[(d^2/4)(\theta - \sin\theta\cos\theta) \right]^{5/3}}{d^{2/3}\theta^{2/3}}$$

Setting

$$\frac{d}{d\theta}\left(AR^{2/3} \right) = 0$$

we obtain on simplification

$$3\theta - 5\theta \cos 2\theta + \sin 2\theta = 0$$

which, when solved by the Newton-Raphson trial-and-error procedure, gives

$$\theta = 2 \cdot 639 \text{ radians} = 151 \cdot 2°$$

(see Appendix A, section A.1).
From Eq. (2.8a),

$$\frac{y}{d} = 0 \cdot 938$$

This is the depth-to-diameter ratio for maximum conveyance of a circular pipe.

2.6   Mean velocity of flow and rate of discharge

The shear resistance, which is a property of real fluids, causes the velocity to vary within the cross section of a channel. It will be found that the manner in which the velocity varies depends on whether the flow is laminar or turbulent, and whether the turbulence itself is smooth or rough (see Chapter 4). The velocity in laminar flow varies according to the parabolic law while, in both types of turbulent flow, it varies according to the logarithmic law. The laws of velocity distribution, which are derived in Chapter 4, are:
for smooth turbulence

$$\frac{u}{u_*} = 5 \cdot 5 + 2 \cdot 5 \ln \frac{y u_*}{v} \tag{2.16}$$

for rough turbulence

$$\frac{u}{u_*} = 8 \cdot 5 + 2 \cdot 5 \ln \frac{y}{k_s} \tag{2.17}$$

where y = distance of a fluid particle from the solid boundary

u_* = shear velocity = $\sqrt{gRS_0}$
v = kinematic viscosity
k_s = height of equivalent sand roughness

The *mean velocity of flow* U is defined by the integral

$$U = \frac{1}{A} \int_A u \, dA \tag{2.18}$$

where A is the cross-sectional area of flow.

It is to be noted that Eqs (2.16) and (2.17) express the velocity as a function only of the depth of flow, and the velocity variation in the lateral direction, being of lower order of magnitude, is ignored.

Disregarding the flow in the laminar sub-layer, the integral represents the actual *rate of discharge Q*, so that Eq. (2.18) can be written as

$$U = \frac{Q}{A} \tag{2.19}$$

which is the relationship universally used in channel-flow calculations. The value of the integral in Eq. (2.18) depends on the geometry of the cross section. However, it has been verified that, by replacing the linear dimension involved in the integrated function by the hydraulic radius, a single law can be applied to all geometric shapes, that is, one for all smooth channels, and another for all rough channels. The derivation of the mean velocity for various channel shapes is given in Chapter 4.

2.7 Mechanism of flow

The basic requirements for flow to take place in a channel are, for the water to have an altitude to initiate the flow and, for the channel to have a gradient to sustain it. The term *upstream end* is applied to the highest point of the channel. In the ensuing flow, the three basic energies, namely, the potential energy, the kinetic energy and the pressure energy, maintain the energy balance. However, for as long as the flow exists, there is a continuous loss of the potential energy that the water has acquired initially by virtue of the altitude. It should be noted that, unlike pipes running under pressure, the pressure energy in an open channel is due only to the depth of water and, therefore, is less significant.

The two forces that largely dominate the flow in a drainage channel are:

(a) The *gravitational force,* which is the weight of the flow, and a useful outcome of the loss of the potential energy.
(b) The *force of friction,* which is due to the roughness of the channel surface, and turbulence, is an inseparable part of the flow mechanism.

The component of the gravitational force that contributes to the flow is proportional to the channel gradient, while the frictional force is proportional to the square of the mean velocity of flow. In an ideal situation, the equilibrium is maintained between the gravitational force, and the frictional force. This is the case of *uniform flow.* The depth of water in a uniform flow is constant, but not so in a varied flow. Here, a third force, the *unbalanced hydrostatic force,* which acts from one cross section of flow to the next, also becomes operative.

Among the three forces just described, the gravitational force is a body force, and so it acts on the volume of flow. The frictional force is concentrated in a narrow region next to the surface of contact between the water and the channel. The hydrostatic force is distributed over the area of the cross section.

By virtue of the flow having a mass, there is also momentum associated with the flow. In the case of varied flow, the momentum also changes along the length of the channel, generating an *inertial force*. According to the law of momentum, the inertial force is the resultant of the three forces constituting the fluid mechanism. Let us begin with the derivation for the inertial force by applying the law of momentum.

As far as the fluid properties are concerned, the two most influential in the flow mechanism are the density and viscosity. Water, which is the only fluid considered in this book, has a bulk modulus of 2.2 Gpa at 20°C, and is considered incompressible.

2.8   The law of momentum, the inertial force

Figure 2.5 shows a volume of flow between two cross sections of a channel, one at an arbitrary distance x from the upstream end, and the other at a small distance δx further downstream. Let the average area of cross section and the mean velocity of the volume be A and U, respectively. The momentum δM associated with the volume is given by

$$\delta M = (\rho A \delta x) U$$

If δx is sufficiently small then the *momentum flux* across the volume, that is, the change of momentum per unit time, will represent also the momentum flux M_f across the cross section at x. Hence,

$$M_f = \frac{\delta M}{\delta t} = \rho A \frac{\delta x}{\delta t} U$$

that is,

$$M_f = \rho A U^2 = \rho \frac{Q^2}{A} \tag{2.20}$$

According to the law of momentum, the inertial force in the forward direction is equal to the time rate of increase of momentum, or the net increase of momentum flux. Hence, if both A and U are constant, the momentum flux will also be constant, and there will be no inertial force acting anywhere along the length of the channel. This is typical of a uniform flow. However, if the flow varies, then the momentum flux

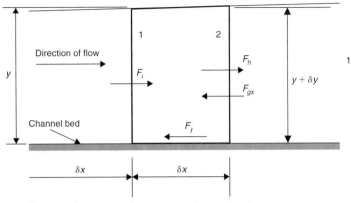

Figure 2.5 *Forces acting on an elementary volume of water.*

changes from section to section, and one has to consider the area and the velocity at the cross sections involved. For instance, if the volume shown in Fig. 2.5 is a finite volume, defined by sections 1 and 2 (2 downstream of 1) having individual values A_1, A_2, U_1 and U_2, then the increase of momentum flux ΔM_f from section 1 to section 2 will be given by the equation

$$\Delta M_f = \rho\left(A_2 U_2^2 - A_1 U_1^2 \right)$$

which, by definition, will also be the inertial force F_i acting on the volume. Hence,

$$F_i = \rho\left(A_2 U_2^2 - A_1 U_1^2 \right) \tag{2.21}$$

Since the discharge rate Q and the area A in a linear drainage channel vary continuously, Eq. (2.21) can be written as

$$F_i = \delta M_f = \rho\delta(AU^2) = \rho\delta\left(\frac{Q^2}{A} \right)$$

$$= \rho\frac{d}{dx}\left(\frac{Q^2}{A} \right)\delta x$$

$$= \rho\left(\frac{2Q}{A}\frac{dQ}{dx} - \frac{Q^2}{A^2}\frac{dA}{dx} \right)\delta x$$

$$= \rho\left(\frac{2Q}{A}\frac{dQ}{dx} - \frac{Q^2}{A^2}\frac{dA}{dy}\frac{dy}{dx} \right)\delta x$$

Using the relationship

$$\frac{dA}{dy} = T = \frac{A}{D}$$

this equation reduces to

$$F_i = \rho \left(\frac{2Q}{A} \frac{dQ}{dx} - \frac{Q^2}{AD} \frac{dy}{dx} \right) \delta x \tag{2.22}$$

This expression for the inertial force will be used later in the derivation of the equation of varied flow.

2.9 Other forces

For the definition of other forces, described in section 2.7, again refer to Fig. 2.5, with the understanding that δx is sufficiently small, so that the hydraulic properties of the cross section at $x + \delta x$ can be obtained from those of the cross section at x by adding only the first order increments. The volume V of the water passing between the two cross sections (in time δt) is given by

$$V = Q\delta t = A\delta x \tag{2.23}$$

where A and Q are the values at section A.

2.9.1 Gravitational force

The gravitational force F_g acting on the volume of water contained within the two cross sections is the weight of the water, that is,

$$F_g = \gamma A \delta x \tag{2.24}$$

The force, which actually causes the flow, is the component of the gravitational force in the direction of flow. Denoting this component by F_{gx}, we have

$$F_{gx} = -(\gamma A \delta x) \frac{dz}{dx}$$

the negative sign indicating that z decreases with increase in x. Recalling Eq. (2.1) for the definition of the channel gradient S_0, this equation becomes

$$F_{gx} = (\gamma A \delta x) S_0 \tag{2.25}$$

2.9.2   Frictional force

The frictional or shear force in a channel is generated by the roughness of the wall and the turbulence of the flow, and is maximum at the wall. This value is assumed to be constant over the entire cross section. It is further assumed that the wall is uniformly rough, so that the wall shear stress is represented by its average value τ_0 defined by the equation

$$\tau_0 = \frac{1}{P}\int_P \tau ds \tag{2.26}$$

where ds is the elementary arc of the wetted perimeter P. The frictional force F_f acting on a length δx of flow is then given by

$$F_f = \tau_0 P \delta x \tag{2.27}$$

In the special case of uniform flow, the shear force balances the gravitational force. Hence, by equating the right-hand sides of Eqs (2.25) and (2.27),

$$\tau_0 = \gamma R S_0 \tag{2.28}$$

2.9.3   Hydrostatic force

A volume of water shown is also subjected to hydrostatic force on either side, and due to the variation of the depth of flow, these forces will, in general, not be of same magnitude. Let the unbalanced component acting on the elementary volume shown in Fig. 2.5 be F_h. Then

$$F_h = \gamma \delta(A\bar{y}) \tag{2.29}$$

where $\bar{y}$ is the depth of the centroid of the area of cross section A. The substitution in this equation of the definition of $\bar{y}$

$$\bar{y} = \frac{1}{A}\int_A y dA$$

results in

$$F_h = \gamma \delta \int_A y dA = \gamma \int_A \left[\delta y dA + y\delta(dA)\right]$$

Neglecting the small quantity of the second order:

$$F_h = \gamma A \delta y \tag{2.30}$$

The hydrostatic force acts in the direction of decreasing y.

2.10   Momentum equation, specific force

In situations where only a short length of a channel is to be considered, for instance, at a hydraulic jump, it can be assumed that the only force contributing to the mechanism of flow is the differential hydrostatic force. In order to represent such a situation mathematically, Eqs (2.29) and (2.21) are written, respectively, as

$$F_h = \rho g(A_2 \bar{y}_2 - A_1 \bar{y}_1) \tag{2.31}$$

$$F_i = \rho \left(\frac{Q_2^2}{A_2} - \frac{Q_1^2}{A_1} \right) \tag{2.32}$$

By setting $Q_2 = Q_1 = Q$, and equating the right-hand sides of these equations, the following *momentum equation* is obtained:

$$\frac{Q^2}{gA_1} + A_1 \bar{y}_1 = \frac{Q^2}{gA_2} + A_2 \bar{y}_2 \tag{2.33}$$

This equation, which is derived from the law of momentum, ensures the equilibrium of flow within a short length of a channel. It also indicates the existence of a force of magnitude per unit weight Σ given by

$$\Sigma = \frac{Q^2}{gA} + A\bar{y} \tag{2.34}$$

This force is called the *specific force*.

It is significant that the momentum equation does not contain any losses and, because of this, it is useful in the derivation of the equation for hydraulic jump (see section 7.7).

2.11   Specific energy

The development of the varied flow theory is closely related to the conception of the *specific energy* of flow. In order to define the specific energy, one has to recall the definition of total energy as the sum of kinetic, potential and pressure energies.

The *kinetic energy* E_k carried per unit time by a volume of water is given by

$$E_k = \frac{1}{2}\rho Q U^2 = \frac{1}{2}\rho A U^3 \tag{2.35}$$

The *potential energy* E_{pot} is due to the altitude of water above an arbitrary datum, and its value per unit time is given by

$$E_{pot} = \gamma AUz \tag{2.36}$$

The *pressure energy* E_{pr} is due to depth of water above the channel bed, and its value per unit volume is given by

$$E_{pr} = \gamma AUy \tag{2.37}$$

By adding the right-hand sides of Eqs (2.35), (2.36) and (2.37), the *total energy E* passing through the area *A* per unit time is obtained. That is,

$$E = \frac{1}{2}\rho AU^3 + \gamma AUz + \gamma AUy \tag{2.38}$$

The division of Eq. (2.38) by $W = \gamma AU$, which is the weight of water passing through the area *A* per unit time, gives the total energy per unit weight of water, or the total head *H*, that is,

$$H = \frac{1}{2}\frac{U^2}{g} + z + y \tag{2.39}$$

The plot of *H* against *x*, shown in Fig. 2.6, is the *energy-grade line*. If we suppose that the head loss due to friction between sections 1 and 2 (see Fig. 2.6) is δh_f, and apply Bernoulli's theorem, we obtain

$$H_2 = H_1 - \delta h_f$$

By taking

$$H_2 = H_1 + \frac{dH}{dx}\delta x$$

we find the loss of total head over a unit length

$$\frac{\delta h_f}{\delta x} = -\frac{dH}{dx} \tag{2.40}$$

where dH/dx is the slope of the energy-grade line.

When the flow is uniform, the only variable on the right-hand side of Eq. (2.39) is *z*, and

$$\frac{dH}{dx} = \frac{dz}{dx} \tag{2.41}$$

which shows that the energy-grade line is parallel to channel bed. It follows that, in the case of uniform flow, the energy-grade line, the water surface and the channel bed are all parallel.

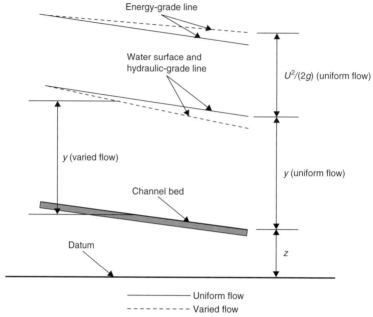

Figure 2.6 *Energy and hydraulic-grade lines.*

The partial sum $z + y$ on the right-hand side of Eq. (2.39) is the piezometric head H_h, which, when plotted against x, yields the *hydraulic-grade line*, also shown in Fig. 2.6. In an open channel, the hydraulic-grade line lies in the free surface and, in the case of uniform flow, is parallel to the energy-grade line. In the case of varied flow, both energy and hydraulic-grade lines are curved, showing the variation of the quantities involved along the length of the channel.

The *specific energy e* is defined as the sum of the hydrostatic and velocity heads, that is, the total energy per unit weight when the datum is taken as the bed of the channel:

$$e = y + \frac{U^2}{2g} \tag{2.42}$$

or, in terms of the rate of discharge,

$$e = y + \frac{Q^2}{2gA^2} \tag{2.43}$$

From this equation, it is evident that the specific energy is a polynomial function of the depth of flow. Many useful conclusions are drawn from the variation of specific energy with the depth of flow. These are discussed in Chapter 6.

2.12 Froude and Reynolds numbers

When two forces are involved in a phenomenon, then the ratio of one to the other is often the key parameter which characterizes the outcome. If there are more than two forces involved, then one of the forces is selected, and the ratio of this force to each of the remaining forces, becomes the subject matter for study. If, for instance, a flow is dominated by only gravitational and frictional forces, then their ratio is important. If its value is one, then the resulting flow is uniform. If the ratio is not one then, to keep the balance, there must be other forces operating, in which case the flow cannot remain uniform, and so it varies. In this situation, there is the induced inertial force, which maintains the balance, and which can be used as the force to calculate the ratios, which are

$$\frac{\text{inertial force}}{\text{gravitational force}} \quad \text{and} \quad \frac{\text{inertial force}}{\text{frictional force}}$$

where the square root of the first ratio is called the Froude number, F, and the second ratio the Reynolds number, R. The mathematical expressions for these dimensionless parameters are derived as follows.

2.12.1 Froude number

Writing Eq. (2.21) as

$$F_i = \rho \frac{d}{dx}(AU^2)\delta x = \rho A \frac{dU^2}{dx} \delta x$$

the inertial force f_i per unit volume is found to be

$$f_i = \rho \frac{dU^2}{dx}$$

Assuming that the derivative of U^2 in the direction of flow can be related to a *characteristic length*, l_c, of the channel cross section, such that

$$\frac{dU^2}{dx} = \frac{U^2}{l_c}$$

the inertial force per unit volume can be expressed as

$$f_i = \rho \frac{U^2}{l_c} \tag{2.44}$$

From Eq. (2.25), the gravitational force per unit volume is γ (ignoring the slope S_0). Hence, the ratio between inertial and gravitational forces per unit volume is

$$\frac{f_i}{f_g} = \frac{U^2}{gl_c}$$

The square root of the expression on the right-hand side of this equation is the Froude number, F. In channel flow, the characteristic length l_c is taken as the hydraulic depth D of the section, and the Froude number is defined as

$$F = \frac{U}{\sqrt{gD}} \tag{2.45}$$

The Froude number identifies the flow as sub-critical or super-critical according to whether it is less, or greater than unity. The flow is described as critical when $F = 1$, that is, when

$$U = \sqrt{gD} \tag{2.46}$$

For a rectangular channel, $D = y$, and the quantity $\sqrt{gy}$ is the wave velocity or *celerity* of the gravity wave. This leads to an alternative definition of Froude number as the ratio of the main stream velocity to the wave velocity.

The following alternative expressions for the Froude number are also used.

$$F = \frac{Q}{A\sqrt{gD}} \tag{2.47}$$

$$F = Q\sqrt{\frac{T}{gA^3}} \tag{2.48}$$

These expressions are self explanatory.

2.12.2 Reynolds number

When viscosity is the major contributory to the resistance to flow, the frictional force f_f acting on a unit volume of flow (Fig. 2.7) is given by

$$f_f = \frac{d\tau}{dy}$$

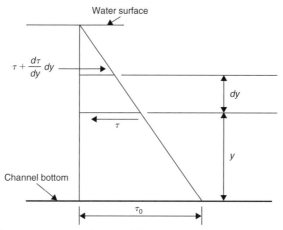

Figure 2.7 *Shear stress on an element of flow.*

On applying Newton's law of viscosity, this equation leads to

$$f_f = \mu \frac{d^2 u}{dy^2}$$

Assuming that the measure of the second derivative of u in the transverse direction is the quantity U/l_c^2 where l_c is a characteristic linear dimension:

$$f_f = \mu \frac{U}{l_c^2} \tag{2.49}$$

The ratio of inertial force to the force due to viscosity is defined as the Reynolds number R. Hence, derived from Eqs (2.44) and (2.49)

$$R = \frac{\rho U^2 / l_c}{\mu U / l_c^2}$$

that is,

$$R = \frac{U l_c}{\upsilon} \tag{2.50}$$

where υ is the kinematic viscosity.

Conventionally, the characteristic linear dimension l_c in calculating the Reynolds number is taken as the diameter of the pipe in the case of pipe flow, and hydraulic radius in channel flow.

Results from controlled tests on flow through pipes [2.1] show that the transition from laminar to turbulent flow occurs at around $R = 2300$. This value of R is described as the critical Reynolds number R_c. The flow, for which $R < R_c$, is classified as laminar flow, and turbulent if $R > R_c$. Results from further experiments show that the critical value of Reynolds number could be 2000, a value which is now generally accepted for channel flow as well as for pipe flow.

References

[2.1] CHOW V.T., *Open Channel Hydraulics*, McGraw-Hill, Singapore, 1973, ch. 5.

[2.2] HENDERSON F.M., *Open Channel Flow*, Macmillan, New York, 1966.

[2.3] FRENCH, RICHARD H., *Open Channel Hydraulics*, McGraw-Hill, International Edition, 1994, ch. 12.

[2.4] *Equivalent Uniform Value for Channels Having Varying Gradients*, Department of Transport Advice Note HA 37/88.

3

Equations of channel flow

Traditionally, the computation of flow in open channels is based on the uniform flow theory represented by Chezy's and Manning's equations. This chapter gives a brief account of these equations, and the derivation of the equation of the varied flow theory. Both forms of the equation are given, that is, the analytical form derived from basic principles, and the finite form suitable for the numerical solution known as the step method.

3.1 Equation of uniform flow, Chezy's and Manning's formulae

It is a law of nature that where there is a movement there is a resistance. The flow of water is no exception. The potential energy which causes the flow by introducing a gravitational force is consumed while overcoming the force of resistance which, in accordance with the law, accompanies the flow. These two forces, therefore, constitute the main members of the equation of flow. Let us begin with the equation of the uniform flow.

The two assumptions that are central to the derivation of the equation of the uniform flow are:

(a) The force of resistance is in perfect balance with the component of the gravitational force acting in the direction of flow.
(b) The force of resistance per unit cross-sectional area of flow is proportional to the square of the velocity of flow.

While we have used the assumption (a) in constructing Eq. (2.28)

$$\tau_0 = \gamma R S_0 \tag{2.28}$$

the assumption (b) means

$$\tau_0 = K_R U^2 \tag{3.1}$$

where K_R is a coefficient of resistance. By eliminating τ_0 between Eqs (2.28) and (3.1), we obtain

$$S_0 = \frac{K_R}{\gamma R} U^2 \tag{3.2}$$

that is,

$$U = C\sqrt{RS_0} \tag{3.3}$$

where

$$C = \sqrt{\frac{\gamma}{K_R}} \tag{3.4}$$

Equation (3.3) is the uniform flow equation, first given by Chezy (c.1770). It is known as the Chezy formula in which the constant C, referred to as Chezy's C, is attributed to the roughness experienced by the flow. The dimensions of C determined from, say, Eq. (3.3) are $L^{1/2}T^{-1}$.

Over the years, the Chezy formula has been subject to modification. As a consequence, the constant C can be expressed in various ways, see for instance sections 5.5 and 5.6 of reference [2.1]. Most popular among these expressions is the Manning's formula (1889)

$$U = \frac{1}{n} R^{2/3} S_0^{1/2} \tag{3.5}$$

In this equation, the constant n is called the roughness factor, or simply, Manning's n. It can be verified that, by taking

$$n = \frac{1}{C} R^{1/6} \tag{3.6}$$

Eq. (3.5) reduces to Eq. (3.3), thus establishing the congruence of these equations. That is, if one of these equations is applied, the other is automatically applied. The dimensions of n are $L^{-1/3}T$. The elimination of C between Eqs (3.4) and (3.6) gives

$$K_R = \frac{\gamma n^2}{R^{1/3}} \tag{3.7}$$

The magnitude of Manning's n depends on several variables, the more important among them being the roughness of the channel surface, and the shape and dimensions of its cross section. This introduces an element of uncertainty in determining the true value of n, and it has been a common practice to consult an authentic table from which, using engineering judgement, an appropriate value is selected. One such table is given on pages 110 to 113 of [3.1].

A rational method to determine the value of n is derived from the law of resistance to flow. This method, which effectively replaces the Manning's equation by a resistance equation, has now been recognized as a conventional method for design of channels as long as the uniform-flow condition is satisfied. However, for the purpose of this chapter, it is assumed that the value of n is known. The law of resistance to flow and its application to flow problems are discussed in Chapter 5.

3.2 Application of the uniform flow equation

The two questions which normally concern a drainage designer are:

(a) The capacity of a drainage channel when the cross-sectional dimensions and the gradient are known.

(b) The depth of flow in a channel for a given discharge.

While the requirement of (a) can be answered directly from the uniform flow equation, Eq. (3.5), the answer to (b) is obtained by first rewriting Eq. (3.5) in terms of y, which operation requires the relationship between R and y, and then solve the equation to determine y. The depth of flow, obtained in this way, is called the *normal depth*, and it is denoted by y_n.

3.2.1 Capacity of a drainage channel

The discharge carrying capacity of a channel is defined as the product of the area of cross section of the flow and the mean velocity. It can be found immediately from the dimensions of the channel, and the velocity given by Eq. (3.5). Consider the following examples:

Example 3.1: A triangular channel shown in Fig. 3.1 carries the surplus water from the adjoining road surface. If the longitudinal gradient is 0·01, and the depth of water is limited to 0·15 m, calculate the maximum discharge. Assume $n = 0·013$.

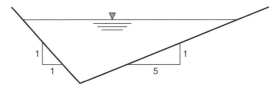

Figure 3.1 *Triangular channel of Example 3.1.*

Solution:

$$m_1 = 1{\cdot}0 \qquad m_2 = 5{\cdot}0 \qquad y = 0{\cdot}15\,\text{m}$$

From Eqs (2.6a) and (2.6e), we have

$$A = 3(0{\cdot}15)^2 = 0{\cdot}0675\,\text{m}^2$$

$$R = \frac{3(0{\cdot}15)}{\sqrt{2} + \sqrt{26}} = 0{\cdot}0691\,\text{m}$$

From Eq. (3.5)

$$U = \frac{(0{\cdot}0691)^{2/3}(0{\cdot}1)}{0{\cdot}013} = 1{\cdot}2953\,\text{m/s}$$

Therefore,

$$Q = UA = 1{\cdot}2953 \times 0{\cdot}0675$$
$$= 0{\cdot}0874\,\text{m}^3/\text{s} = 87{\cdot}4\,\text{l/s}$$

Example 3.2: Determine the capacity of a circular pipe, of internal diameter 1·0 m, laid at a longitudinal gradient of 0·01. Assume $n = 0{\cdot}013$.

Solution:
For maximum capacity of a circular pipe

$$y = 0{\cdot}938d$$

$$\theta = 151{\cdot}2° = 2{\cdot}639^R \qquad \text{(see section 2.5.3)}$$

From Eq. (2.8b)

$$A = \frac{1}{4}(2{\cdot}639 + 0{\cdot}42216)(1{\cdot}0) = 0{\cdot}765\,\text{m}^2$$

From Eq. (2.8d)

$$P = 2{\cdot}639 \times 1{\cdot}0 = 2{\cdot}639\,\text{m}$$

Therefore,

$$R = 0{\cdot}765/2{\cdot}639 = 0{\cdot}290\,\text{m}$$

From Eq. (3.5)

$$U = \frac{(0{\cdot}29)^{2/3}(0{\cdot}1)}{0{\cdot}013} = 3{\cdot}37\,\text{m/s}$$

Therefore

$$Q = 3\cdot37 \times 0\cdot765 = 2\cdot58 \, \text{m}^3/\text{s}$$

3.2.2 Normal depth of flow in a drainage channel

Given the maximum discharge rate, it is sometimes required to determine the depth of flow. For this, Eq. (3.5) is rewritten so that all geometric parameters are expressed in terms of the normal depth y_n, and then, the resulting equation is solved for y_n. In the case of an open channel, the quantity $AR^{2/3}$, which is the measure of discharge (see section 2.5), increases with the depth and, hence, the solution of Eq. (3.5) is unique. That is, for a given combination of Q, n and S_0, there is only one value of y_n. In the case of a closed conduit, the value of $AR^{2/3}$ first increases with the depth, reaches its maximum, and then decreases as the depth approaches the full value. In a circular pipe, for instance, the discharge is maximum at $y/d = 0\cdot938$. In any event, due to the occurrence of $R^{2/3}$, Eq. (3.5) can be solved only numerically. For instance, if we chose to apply the Newton-Raphson method, we have to write this equation as

$$F(y_n) = A^{5/2} - \left(\frac{nQ}{\sqrt{S_0}}\right)^{3/2} P = 0 \tag{3.8}$$

and, for a rectangular or trapezoidal channels, use the initial trial value of y_{n0} of y as

$$y_{n0} = \left(\frac{nQ/\sqrt{S_0}}{B}\right)^{0\cdot6} \tag{3.9}$$

Example 3.3: A rectangular channel $1\cdot5$ m wide is laid at a uniform gradient of $1{:}100$. If the discharge capacity of the channel is $2\,\text{m}^3/\text{s}$, using the Manning's formula calculate the normal depth ($n = 0\cdot015$).

Solution:

$$A = 1\cdot5y \qquad P = 1\cdot5 + 2y$$

$$\frac{nQ}{\sqrt{S_0}} = \frac{0\cdot015 \times 2\cdot0}{0\cdot1} = 0\cdot3$$

The substitution of this, and the expressions for A and P into Eq. (3.8) gives

$$F(y_n) = 2\cdot7557\, y_n^{5/2} - 0\cdot3286 y_n - 0\cdot2465 \tag{i}$$

An initial trial value of y_{n0} can be obtained from Eq. (3.9), that is,

$$y_{n0} = \left(\frac{nQ/\sqrt{S_0}}{B} \right)^{0\cdot6} = \left(\frac{0\cdot3}{1\cdot5} \right)^{0\cdot6} = 0\cdot38$$

From the Newton-Raphson method (Appendix A), the following values after first three iterations are obtained:

$$y_{n1} = 0\cdot4781\,\text{m} \qquad y_{n2} = 0\cdot4617\,\text{m} \qquad y_{n3} = 0\cdot4612\,\text{m}$$

When the last value is substituted in Eq. (i), $F(y_n) = 0\cdot00005$ is obtained. Since this is sufficiently close to zero, it can be inferred that $y_{n3} = 0\cdot4612\,\text{m}$ is sufficiently accurate.

Example 3.4: Using the Manning's formula, determine the normal depth of a trapezoidal channel from the following data:

$$B = 1\cdot5\,\text{m}$$
$$m_1 = m_2 = 1\cdot0$$
$$S_0 = 0\cdot0025$$
$$Q = 10\,\text{m}^3/\text{s}$$
$$n = 0\cdot0125$$

Solution:

$$A = \left[B + \frac{1}{2}(m_1 + m_2)y \right] y = (1\cdot5 + y)y$$

$$P = B + y\sqrt{1 + m_1^2} + y\sqrt{1 + m_2^2} = 1\cdot5 + 2\cdot828y$$

$$\frac{nQ}{\sqrt{S_0}} = \frac{0\cdot0125 \times 10\cdot0}{0\cdot05} = 2\cdot5$$

From Eq. (3.8)

$$F(y_n) = (1\cdot5y_n + y_n^2)^{5/2} - 11\cdot17y_n - 5\cdot93 \qquad \text{(i)}$$

Starting with a trial value

$$y_{n0} = \left(\frac{nQ/\sqrt{S_0}}{B} \right)^{0\cdot6} = \left(\frac{2\cdot5}{1\cdot5} \right)^{0\cdot6} = 1\cdot36$$

we obtain

after first iteration	$y_{n1} = 1.235\,\text{m}$
after second iteration	$y_{n2} = 1.2104\,\text{m}$
after third iteration	$y_{n3} = 1.2095\,\text{m}$

The substitution of the last value in Eq. (i) above, gives $F(y_3) = 0.0017$.

Accepting this as the tolerance in the value of F, three iterations give sufficiently accurate values of y_n.

Example 3.5: Determine the internal diameter of a circular pipe to carry a discharge of $10\,\text{m}^3/\text{s}$, laid at a longitudinal gradient of 0.0025. Assume $n = 0.013$.

Solution:

For maximum capacity of a circular pipe, $y = 0.938\,d$, that is, $\theta = 151.2° = 2.639^R$

From Eqs (2.8b) and (2.8f)

$$AR^{2/3} = \left(\frac{1}{4}\right)^{5/3} \frac{(\theta - \sin\theta\cos\theta)^{5/3}}{\theta^{2/3}} d^{8/3} = 0.3353\,d^{8/3}$$

From Eq. (3.5)

$$Q = AU = \frac{(0.3353)(0.05)}{0.013}d^{8/3} = 10$$

Therefore

$$d = \left(\frac{10 \times 0.013}{0.3353 \times 0.05}\right)^{3/8} = 2.2\,\text{m}$$

3.3 Friction slope

In dealing with varied flow, it has been found expedient to use the Manning formula as a way of relating the maximum shear stress to the mean velocity of flow. This is effected by introducing a parameter called *friction slope* S_f:

$$U = \frac{1}{n}R^{2/3}S_f^{1/2} \tag{3.10}$$

which leads to the following definition of S_f:

$$S_f = \frac{n^2 U^2}{R^{4/3}} = \frac{n^2 Q^2}{A^2 R^{4/3}} \tag{3.11}$$

The maximum shear stress is obtained by substituting the expressions for U and K_R from Eqs (3.5) and (3.7), respectively, into Eq. (3.1), and replacing S_0 by S_f. This gives

$$\tau_0 = \frac{\gamma n^2}{R^{1/3}} \frac{R^{4/3}}{n^2} S_f = \gamma R S_f \qquad (3.12)$$

The frictional force is then given by

$$F_f = \gamma P R S_f \delta x = \gamma A S_f \delta x \qquad (3.13)$$

Since, the head loss per unit length due to friction is

$$\frac{h_f}{\delta x} = \frac{F_f}{\lambda A \delta x} = S_f \qquad (3.14)$$

the physical interpretation of the friction slope is that it is the slope of the energy-grade line (see section 2.11).

3.4 Equation of varied flow

Any variation in the discharge rate, say, due to inflow, causes the depth of flow to vary, and disturbs the balance between gravitational and frictional forces. The force balance can be restored only by the inclusion of the inertial force and, as a consequence, Eq. (3.3) loses its validity. The equation of motion for varied flow is derived by adding the components of gravity, hydrostatic and frictional forces, in the direction of the flow, and equating the sum to the inertial force. Recalling the expressions for these forces from Eqs (2.25), (2.30), (3.13) and (2.22)

$$F_{gx} = (\gamma A \delta x) S_0 \qquad (2.25)$$

$$F_h = \gamma A \delta y \qquad (2.30)$$

$$F_f = \gamma A S_f \delta x \qquad (3.13)$$

$$F_i = \rho \left(\frac{2Q}{A} \frac{dQ}{dx} - \frac{Q^2}{AD} \frac{dy}{dx} \right) \delta x \qquad (2.22)$$

the following equation is constructed:

$$\rho \left(\frac{2Q}{A} \frac{dQ}{dx} - \frac{Q^2}{AD} \frac{dy}{dx} \right) \delta x = \gamma A S_0 \delta x - \gamma A S_f \delta x - \gamma A \delta y$$

which on dividing by $\gamma A \delta x$, and taking limit as δx approaches zero, yields

$$\frac{dy}{dx} = \frac{S_0 - S_f - (2Q/gA^2)(dQ/dx)}{1 - (Q^2/gA^2 D)} \tag{3.15}$$

This differential equation is known as the *differential equation of varied flow*, which, being of the first order in y, can be solved only if the depth of flow y is known at some point. This point is conveniently called the *control section*. It will be found that, if the gradient of the channel does not exceed a certain value then the downstream end of the channel acts as a control section where the depth could be determined from the rate of discharge at the outlet and the dimensions of the cross section. However, for steeper slopes, the control section moves upwards, and it becomes necessary to locate it. This is dealt with in Chapter 8.

Furthermore, since the right-hand side of Eq. (3.15) contains (implicitly) the unknown y, its solution can be approached only by numerical means, and it becomes necessary to translate this equation into its finite version (see the following section). The method which employes the finite version in the numerical determination of y is known as *the step method*.

3.5   Equation for the step method

Consider the volume of water flowing between cross sections A and B (Fig. 3.2), B at a distance δx, downstream of A. The segment δx is called the *step length*. Let, at section A

A_a = area of flow,
U_a = mean velocity of flow,
Q_a = discharge rate,

and let A_b, U_b, and Q_b be the corresponding values at section B.

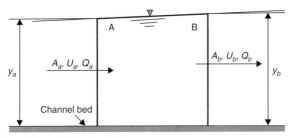

Figure 3.2 *Flow through the step AB.*

The inertial force F_i acting on the volume, in the downstream direction, is given by Eq. (2.21), that is

$$F_i = \rho(A_b U_b^2 - A_a U_a^2) = \rho(Q_b U_b - Q_a U_a) \tag{3.16}$$

By definition, F_i is also the resultant of all forces (i.e., gravitational, hydrostatic and frictional) acting on the volume, in the direction of flow:

$$F_i = F_{gx} + F_f + F_h$$

If the component forces are taken as arithmetic averages of the values on either side of the step, then we have

from Eq. (2.25)

$$F_{gx} = \frac{1}{2}\gamma(A_a + A_b)S_0\delta x$$

from Eq. (2.30)

$$F_h = -\frac{1}{2}\gamma(A_b + A_a)(y_b - y_a)$$

The negative sign on the right-hand side of this equation is justified if it is assumed that $y_b > y_a$.

From Eq. (3.13)

$$F_f = -\frac{1}{2}\gamma(A_a S_{fa} + A_b S_{fb})\delta x$$

Here, the negative sign indicates that the frictional force acts in the direction opposite to that of the flow.

Equating the sum of the expressions for the forces to the right-hand member of Eq. (3.16), we obtain

$$\frac{1}{g}(Q_b U_b - Q_a U_a) - \frac{1}{2}S_0(A_a + A_b)\delta x$$

$$+ \frac{1}{2}(A_a S_{fa} + A_b S_{fb})\delta x + \frac{1}{2}(A_b + A_a)(y_b - y_a) = 0 \tag{3.17}$$

This is the equation for the step method. It relates the hydraulic properties at any two cross sections, and is central to the computation of *flow profiles*. Starting the first step at the control section (where the hydraulic properties are known), and assuming a suitable step length, Eq. (3.17) is solved for the depth of flow at the end of the step. The end of the first step is then taken as the beginning of the second step, and so forth. The procedure is continued until the depth along the entire length of the channel is determined. The application of the step method is discussed in detail in Chapter 7.

The differential equation of varied flow, Eq. (3.12), can also be derived by dividing the left-hand side of Eq. (3.16) by δx, and taking limit of the quotient as δx tends to zero. Thus we obtain

$$\frac{1}{g}\frac{d}{dx}(QU) + A\frac{dy}{dx} = (S_0 - S_f)A$$

that is,

$$\frac{1}{g}\frac{d}{dx}\left(\frac{Q^2}{A}\right) + A\frac{dy}{dx} = (S_0 - S_f)A$$

that is,

$$\frac{1}{g}\left(\frac{2Q}{A}\frac{dQ}{dx} - \frac{Q^2}{A^2}\frac{dA}{dy}\frac{dy}{dx}\right) + A\frac{dy}{dx} = (S_0 - S_f)A$$

which reduces to Eq. (3.15).

4

Resistance to flow in open channels: velocity distribution laws

Starting from Prandtl's mixing length theory, this chapter contains the derivation of laws of velocity distribution in both smooth and rough turbulence. The law is then applied to circular, rectangular and triangular cross sections. It has been demonstrated that if the linear dimension representing the cross section of flow is replaced by the hydraulic radius, then the same laws of velocity distribution (for smooth and rough turbulence) can be applied to channels of arbitrary shapes.

4.1 Resistance to flow

The source that contributes most to the overall resistance to flow in a channel is the friction generated by the roughness of the channel surface and turbulence of the flow. There are also incidental sources of resistance, such as expansion or contraction of the cross section and any change of the alignment of the channel. The loss of head due to any of these is expressed as a multiple of the dynamic head.

The computation of flow in open channels is normally carried out on the assumption that the flow characteristics, velocity and depth, for instance, do not change along the length of the channel, thus allowing the use of the uniform flow theory. The respective coefficients, C and n, in Chezy's and Manning's equations represent the total friction. The friction generates shear stress, and a major consequence of the shear stress is the variation of velocity over the cross section of the flow. From this it follows that the magnitudes of C and n must depend on the degree of interaction between the shear stress and the velocity of flow. This interaction is referred to as the *law of resistance* to flow.

Furthermore, since the law of resistance concerns with the mean velocity, rather than its point value (for instance, the familiar Darcy-Weisbach law), it becomes necessary to find out the manner in which the velocity is distributed, so that one can determine the mean velocity of flow, say, through a process of integration. Therefore, it is natural to start the present discussion on resistance to flow with the law of velocity distribution and, since shear stress is the key parameter in the velocity distribution, recall the law of viscosity, which regulates the shear stress.

4.2   Viscosity

The velocity of a moving fluid at the boundary is the same as that of the solid surface the fluid is in contact with. This *no slip condition*, which is satisfied by all real fluids, demonstrates the existence of shear stress at the surface of contact. Real fluids also resist angular deformation imposed by the flow. Thus, shear stress which is not confined to only the contact area is active everywhere within the volume of flow, exceptions being the free surface of water in an open channel, and the axis of a pipe flowing full. The tendency to adhere to solid surfaces, and offering resistance to flow are both due to the fluid property called *viscosity*.

The fluid viscosity dominates the laminar flow by maintaining the continuity of the shear stress from the solid boundary to points within the volume of the flow by generating velocity gradients normal to the direction of the flow. The parameter that represents the viscosity is the coefficient of *dynamic viscosity* μ. The shear stress associated with laminar flow is called *viscous shear stress*, which is denoted by τ_l, the index l indicating laminar flow. The dynamic viscosity relates the viscous shear stress to the velocity gradient in accordance with Newton's law of viscosity. Assuming the flow to be in the x direction, and the depth of flow in the y direction, the viscosity law is expressed by the equation

$$\tau_l = \mu \frac{du}{dy} \tag{4.1}$$

Associated with the dynamic viscosity is the *kinematic viscosity* v, which is the ratio of the dynamic viscosity to the mass density:

$$v = \mu/\rho \tag{4.2}$$

The dimensions of μ and v are, respectively, $ML^{-1}T^{-1}$ and L^2T^{-1}.

The kinematic viscosity represents the viscous force acting on a mass of fluid and its magnitude, relative to the gravitational force, distinguishes between laminar and turbulent flow (see section 2.11.2). However, the viscous shear stress in channel flow is significant only in an extremely thin region next to the solid surface. The main flow is dominated by turbulent shear stress, the Reynolds number being well over 2000.

Analogous to Eq. (4.1), is the equation for turbulent flow:

$$\tau_t = \zeta \frac{du}{dy} \tag{4.3}$$

This equation is based on Prandtl's mixing length theory. The parameter ζ is called the *eddy viscosity* or the *apparent viscosity* for, in turbulent flow, the real viscosity is not of much significance. It will be found later in the chapter that the eddy viscosity is not a fluid property, but depends on the density and a parameter called mixing length.

In the transient region, in which the flow changes from fully laminar to fully turbulent, both viscosity and turbulence contribute to the shear stress. Its magnitude τ is given by

$$\tau = \tau_l + \tau_t = \mu \frac{du}{dy} + \zeta \frac{du}{dy} \tag{4.4}$$

The influence of the first term on the right-hand side of this equation decreases as the distance from the solid boundary increases, while that of the other term increases, until the entire shear stress is due to turbulence.

The mechanism of laminar flow ($R < 2000$) is different from that of turbulent flow ($R > 2000$), and this is reflected in different laws of velocity distribution for laminar and turbulent flows. In laminar flow, the movement of the fluid molecules is slow and orderly and, hence, more amenable to a mathematical formulation. In turbulent flow, the movement is fast and irregular, and it is not possible to analyse it by purely mathematical means. The laws of velocity distribution discussed in the following sections are based on Prandtl's mixing length theory [4.1, 4.2]. Since the outcome of the theory has been substantially verified by means of experimental investigations [4.3, 4.4], these laws are widely accepted as the rational basis for the design of pipes and, after some adjustment to the numerical constants, are also applied to channels of arbitrary shapes.

4.3   Smooth and rough turbulence

The surface of a channel may vary from very smooth to very rough. In order to understand the terms *smooth* and *rough* in the context of channel flow, for these are attributes of the turbulent flow, one has to recognize the existence of a thin layer of fluid, immediately next to the wall, in which the flow is laminar (Fig. 4.1). This layer is called *laminar sub-layer*. In the case of a *smooth channel*, the laminar sub-layer is the only region separating the main body of the flow from the surface of the channel. The flow in this

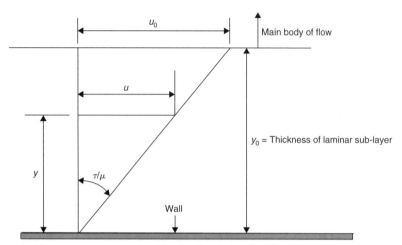

Figure 4.1 *Shear stress and velocity distribution in laminar boundary layer.*

region is dominated by only the wall shear, and the turbulence is described as perfectly smooth. If, however, there are protrusions on the channel surface, one has to consider the average height of these protrusions. In the case of highly rough surface, all protrusions extend beyond the laminar sub-layer, and the turbulence is described as completely rough. In an average situation, some of the protrusions extend beyond the laminar sub-layer while others do not. The turbulence in this situation is described as *transitionally rough*. The mathematical implication of the existence of the laminar sub-layer will soon follow.

4.4   Velocity distribution in turbulent flow

It is believed that, in turbulent flow, the fluid particles move in lumps, which, in addition to the mainstream velocity, have velocity components in the transverse direction. The transverse movement takes each lump of fluid particles from one environment, represented by a velocity field, into the next. This happens in such quick succession that each lump, taking with it the forward momentum of the previous environment, has to travel a length, during which it exchanges its momentum associated with the new environment. The transverse movement of fluid particles also causes a *whirling* or *eddy motion* that results in the mixing of the flow. These two aspects of turbulent flow, namely, the transverse movement of fluid particles, and the exchange of forward momentum are the essential features of Prandtl's *mixing length theory*. According to the theory, the *mixing length* denoted by l, is described as the distance which a fluid particle has to

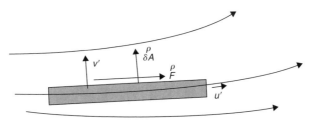

Figure 4.2 *Turbulent shear force on an element of fluid.*

traverse during the exchange of the forward momentum. The turbulent flow is, therefore, an unsteady flow with velocity perturbations (fluctuations) u' and v' in the longitudinal and transverse directions, respectively, superimposed on the mean flow. That is, the velocity of flow appearing in the analysis is the time-averaged value of the actual velocity. These velocity fluctuations indicate the intensity of turbulence. It is assumed that the magnitude of u' and v' are of the same order.

Figure 4.2 shows the fluctuation of the forward velocity of a fluid particle from its value u in a certain environment to $u + (du/dy)l$ in the next. From this we obtain

$$u' = l\frac{du}{dy} \qquad v' \approx u' \tag{4.5}$$

By applying the momentum equation to a small control volume, shown in Fig. 4.2, the shear stress τ_t in the turbulent region can be expressed in terms of u' and v': Consider a lump of fluid particles moving through the control volume, with a forward velocity u' relative to an adjacent lump. The forward momentum per unit mass carried by the fluid particles is also u'. The fluid particles move out of the control volume, in the transverse direction at the flow rate $v'\delta A$, where δA is the area under shear. Hence, the increase in momentum efflux through the control surface is $\rho(v'\delta A)(u')$, which, according to the law of momentum, is the force due to turbulent shear acting in the forward direction, in the plane of δA. Denoting this force by δF_t:

$$\delta F_t = \rho(v'\delta A)(u')$$

Substituting into this the expressions for u' and v' from Eq. (4.5), and dividing the result by δA, we obtain the following relationship between the velocity gradient and the shear stress

$$\tau_t = \frac{\delta F_t}{\delta A} = \rho l^2 \left(\frac{du}{dy}\right)^2 \tag{4.6}$$

that is,

$$\frac{du}{dy} = \frac{1}{l}\sqrt{\frac{\tau_t}{\rho}} \tag{4.7}$$

The integral of this equation is the velocity distribution caused by the turbulent shear stress τ_t. Let us now consider two extreme cases, one of perfectly smooth and the other of completely rough turbulence.

4.5 Velocity distribution in smooth turbulent flow

Treating the smooth turbulence, it is assumed that either there are no protrusions on the channel surface or, if there are, they do not extend beyond the laminar sub-layer. It is further assumed that, within the laminar sub-layer, where, in fact, Eq. (4.1) applies, the velocity gradient satisfies the straight-line relationship

$$\frac{du}{dy} = \frac{u}{y} = \frac{u_0}{y_0} \tag{4.8}$$

where y_0 is the thickness of the laminar sub-layer, and u_0 is the wall velocity which is the name given to the velocity at the common boundary between the laminar sub-layer and the main flow.

From the law of viscosity

$$\left(\frac{du}{dy}\right)_{y=y_0} = \frac{\tau_0}{\mu}$$

in which τ_0 is the shear stress at the boundary between the laminar sub-layer and the rest of the flow. We call this *wall shear stress*.

Hence, we have from Eq. (4.8)

$$\frac{u_0}{y_0} = \frac{\tau_0}{\mu} \tag{4.9}$$

$$u = \frac{u_0}{y_0}y \tag{4.10}$$

and

$$\tau_0 = \frac{u}{y}\mu \quad (y \neq 0) \tag{4.11}$$

We now introduce a parameter u_*, defined by the equation

$$u_* = \sqrt{\frac{\tau_0}{\rho}} \tag{4.12}$$

This parameter is called the *friction velocity* or the *shear velocity.*
Since, $v = \mu/\rho$,

$$\frac{\tau_0}{\mu} = \frac{u_*^2}{v} \tag{4.13}$$

In the case of uniform flow, the wall shear stress is obtained by equating the gravitational and frictional forces, so that

$$\tau_0 = \gamma R S_0 \tag{4.14}$$

which, when substituted in Eq. (4.12), gives

$$u_* = \sqrt{g R S_0} \tag{4.15}$$

This expression for the shear velocity is used regularly in the formulation of the laws of resistance.

Eliminating τ_0/μ between Eqs (4.9) and (4.13),

$$y_0 = \frac{u_0 v}{u_*^2} \tag{4.16}$$

is obtained, which is the thickness of the laminar sub-layer.
Writing Eq. (4.16) as

$$\frac{u_0}{y_0} = \frac{u_*^2}{v} \tag{4.17}$$

and eliminating u_0/y_0 between this equation and Eq. (4.10), the velocity distribution within the laminar sub-layer obtained is

$$\frac{u}{u_*} = \frac{u_*}{v} y \tag{4.18}$$

Recalling Eq. (4.6), and replacing $(du/dy)^2$ by $u'v'/l^2$ (see Eq. (4.5)), we obtain

$$\frac{\tau_t}{\rho} = (u'v')$$

that is,

$$u_* = \sqrt{u'v'} \tag{4.19}$$

This equation demonstrates that the friction velocity is a measure of the intensity of turbulence.

Furthermore, by writing Eq. (4.6) as

$$\tau_t = \left(\rho l^2 \frac{du}{dy} \right) \frac{du}{dy}$$

and using the notation

$$\zeta = \rho l^2 \frac{du}{dy}$$

we obtain the relationship between turbulent shear stress and the velocity gradient normal to the wall

$$\tau_t = \zeta \frac{du}{dy} \tag{4.3}$$

where the coefficient ζ depends on the mass density, the mixing length and the velocity gradient itself. Analogous to the coefficient of dynamic viscosity μ, defined by Eq. (4.1), ζ is the *apparent coefficient of viscosity* or *eddy viscosity* but, unlike μ, it is not a material property.

To proceed with the solution of Eq. (4.7), which is now written as

$$\frac{du}{dy} = \frac{u_*}{l} \tag{4.20}$$

the following two assumptions are made: (*a*) the shear stress outside the laminar sub-layer is of constant value τ_0; and (*b*) the mixing length l is proportional to y, that is,

$$l = \kappa y \tag{4.21}$$

where κ is a dimensionless constant.

The first assumption is justified on physical grounds, that is, due to mixing, the shear stress in the main body of flow is constant. Hence, the stresses τ_t and τ_l have only symbolic difference. The second assumption is also justified, since, there is no velocity fluctuation at the solid boundary and, although, du/dy is not zero there, the turbulent shear stress is zero. It is also consistent with the fact that, along a smooth wall where there is no transverse motion, l must be zero. Along a rough wall, l must be of the order of the height of the roughness.

The elimination of l between Eqs (4.20) and (4.21) gives the following alternative version of Eq. (4.20):

$$\frac{du}{u_*} = \frac{l}{\kappa} \frac{dy}{y} \tag{4.22}$$

It should be mentioned that, by taking the wall shear stress as the representative viscous shear stress for the entire cross section, the validity of Eq. (4.22) is extended beyond the neighbourhood of the wall.

The solution of Eq. (4.22) is

$$\frac{u}{u_*} = \frac{1}{\kappa} \ln \frac{y}{c} \tag{4.23}$$

where the constant of integration c is determined from the condition: At $y = y_0$, $u = u_0$.

Hence, the complete solution of Eq. (4.22) is

$$\frac{u}{u_*} = \frac{u_0}{u_*} + \frac{1}{\kappa} \ln\left(\frac{y}{y_0}\right) \tag{4.24}$$

Eliminating y_0 between Eqs (4.16) and (4.24), we obtain

$$\frac{u}{u_*} = \frac{u_0}{u_*} + \frac{1}{\kappa} \ln\left(\frac{u_*^2}{u_0 v} y\right)$$

that is,

$$\frac{u}{u_*} = \frac{1}{\kappa} \ln\left(\frac{u_* y}{v}\right) + \frac{u_0}{u_*} - \frac{1}{\kappa} \ln\left(\frac{u_0}{u_*}\right) \tag{4.25}$$

Introducing the notation

$$\phi_* = \frac{u}{u_*} \tag{4.26}$$

$$\phi_0 = \frac{u_0}{u_*} - \frac{1}{\kappa} \ln\left(\frac{u_0}{u_*}\right) \tag{4.27}$$

$$\eta_* = \frac{u_*}{v} y \qquad (4.28)$$

Eq. (4.25) is written in the abbreviated form

$$\phi_* = \frac{1}{\kappa} \ln \eta_* + \phi_0 \qquad (4.29)$$

Since, within the laminar sub-layer

$$\frac{u}{u_*} = \frac{1}{u_*}\left(\frac{u_0 y}{y_0}\right) = \frac{1}{u_*}\left(\frac{u_0 u_*^2 y}{u_0 v}\right) = \frac{u_*}{v} y \qquad (4.30)$$

we find that the velocity distribution within the laminar sub-layer can also be expressed as

$$\phi_* = \eta_* \qquad (4.31)$$

It is seen from Eqs (4.25) and (4.29), the solution forms of Eq. (4.22) that, outside of the laminar region, the velocity varies with the distance from the solid surface according to the logarithmic law. This has been verified by Nikuradse's tests on smooth pipes [4.3], performed at Reynolds numbers ranging from 4×10^3 to 3.5×10^6. The measurements taken at points near the wall, and at varying distances up to the axis of the pipes agree with the linear relationship between ϕ_* and $\ln \eta_*$ wherever $\eta_* > 70$ (Fig. 4.3). In the region $\eta_* < 70$, the measurements deviate from the straight line, and follow a downward path. Interpreting $1/\kappa$ and ϕ_0 as the parameters of the straight line representing the data points, these coefficients can be determined only in the region $\eta_* > 70$. Reichardt extended Nikuradse's work for values of η_* smaller than 70, by taking points very close to the wall [4.4] and showed that, for $\eta_* < 5$, the parameters η_* and ϕ_* satisfy Eq. (4.31). The investigations of Nikuradse and Reichardt lead to the following conclusions:

(a) In the region $y < 5v/u_*$, the flow is laminar and, hence, the resistance is mainly due to viscosity.
(b) In the region $y > 70v/u_*$, the flow is fully turbulent and, hence, the resistance due to viscosity is negligible.
(c) In the intermediate region $5v/u_* < y < 70v/u_*$, the flow is transitional, and both viscous and turbulent shears contribute to the resistance.

From (a), we deduce the thickness of the laminar sub-layer as $5v/u_*$.

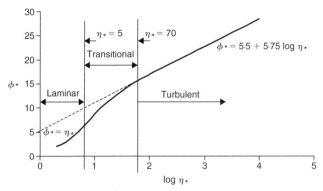

Figure 4.3 *The three regions of flow in a smooth channel.*

From the straight line representing the data points in the turbulent region (Fig. 4.3), we obtain

$$\frac{1}{\kappa} = 2.5 \tag{4.32}$$

and

$$\phi_0 = 5.5 \tag{4.33}$$

Substituting the values of κ and ϕ_0 into Eq. (4.30), we obtain the following velocity distribution for smooth pipes:

$$\phi_* = 2.5 \, ln\,\eta_* + 5.5 = 5.75 \log \eta_* + 5.5 \tag{4.34}$$

or

$$\frac{u}{u_*} = 2.5 \, ln\left(\frac{yu_*}{v}\right) + 5.5 = 5.75 \log \left(\frac{yu_*}{v}\right) + 5.5 \tag{4.35}$$

This equation is the law of velocity distribution in the neighbourhood of the wall. The law is found to be sufficiently accurate also for points further away from the wall. It is to be noticed, however, that this equation cannot satisfy the boundary condition at the wall where $u = 0$, or at the centre line of a pipe running full where $du/dy = 0$. However, these shortcomings are not considered important, for the above velocity distribution is in excellent agreement with measurements.

There are alternatives to the mixing length theory, for instance, one due to von Karman's similarity hypothesis and Taylor's vorticity transport theory. These are not discussed here, but can be found in references [4.2, 4.5].

According to the logarithmic law of velocity distribution, the velocity in an open channel is expected to be maximum at the free surface. However, factors, such as surface roughness and any special features of the channel layout, influence the location of the maximum velocity. There are also secondary flows, into and out of corners in non-circular cross sections, in which case the shape of the cross section becomes more influential in pulling the maximum velocity to a level below the free surface, see page 577 of [4.2]. In very wide and shallow channels the maximum velocity occurs close to the free surface.

4.6   Velocity distribution in completely rough turbulence

The resistance to flow in channels is predominantly due to the roughness of the surface of the channel, and the parameter that represents this property is the average height of roughness. The density of protrusions, described as the number of protrusions per unit surface area, is also important, but the height of roughness is more amenable to analytical treatment. The development of the theory of turbulent flow in channels with rough surfaces is mainly due to Nikuradse's measurements on pipes roughened by means of graded sand grains glued on the inside surface [4.6]. For this reason, the average height of roughness in a given channel is equated to the equivalent sand roughness, and is denoted by k_s. It will be found that the resistance coefficient is a function of the *relative roughness* k_s/d (for pipes), and k_s/R (for non-circular sections, where R is the hydraulic radius), and that the resistance law for flow past rough surfaces depends on the ratio of the average height of roughness to the thickness of the laminar sub-layer $y_0 = 5v/u_*$. This is so because if k_s is less than y_0 then the surface roughness has no significance, and the resistance to flow will be due only to the viscosity. In this situation, the surface is identified as *hydraulically smooth*. Introducing the *roughness Reynolds number*

$$R_k = \frac{u_* k_s}{v} \qquad (4.36)$$

and following the development of flow from laminar to fully turbulent in the light of the conclusions drawn in the previous section, it is possible to classify the surfaces and the associated turbulence regimes in terms of the following limiting values of the roughness Reynolds number:

(a) Smooth ($k_s < y_0$) $R_k < 5$
      The height of roughness is everywhere less than the thickness of the laminar sub-layer, the resistance to flow is due mainly to viscosity,

and the resistance coefficient is a function of only the mainstream Reynolds number.

(b) *Completely rough* $R_k > 70$

The height of roughness is everywhere greater than the thickness of the laminar sub-layer, and the resistance to flow, which is now due to the drag on the protrusions, is proportional to the square of the mean velocity. The resistance coefficient depends now only on the relative roughness k_s/d or k_s/R.

(c) *Transitional* $5 < R_k < 70$

Some protrusions extend beyond the laminar sub-layer, and others remain within it. Hence, only those protrusions, which extend beyond the laminar sub-layer, offer additional resistance to flow due to turbulence and, as a result, both viscosity and turbulence contribute to the resistance to flow. The resistance coefficient now depends on both k_s/d (or k_s/R) and R. Most cases of flow in drainage pipes and channels belong to this category.

The starting point for the derivation of the law of velocity distribution in rough channels must be Eq. (4.23), which is valid for both rough as well as smooth turbulence, but the constant of integration c is to be determined from the condition at $y = \varepsilon k_s$, $u = u_0$, where ε is a coefficient depending on the nature of roughness. Hence, for a rough channel, Eq. (4.25) is replaced by

$$\frac{u}{u_*} = \frac{1}{\kappa} ln\left(\frac{y}{k_s}\right) + \left(\frac{u_0}{u_*} - \frac{1}{\kappa} ln\,\varepsilon\right) \tag{4.37}$$

Using the notation

$$\phi_1 = \frac{u_0}{u_*} - \frac{1}{\kappa} ln\,\varepsilon \tag{4.38}$$

we obtain the velocity distribution in rough turbulence expressed as

$$\frac{u}{u_*} = \frac{1}{\kappa} ln\left(\frac{y}{k_s}\right) + \phi_1 \tag{4.39}$$

The logarithmic law of velocity distribution in rough turbulence has been verified by Nikuradse's measurements on artificially roughened pipes [4.6]. The measurements also provide the numerical values of the constants $\kappa = 0.4$, and $\phi_1 = 8.5$. Since, the value of κ is the same for both smooth and rough turbulence, it confirms that κ is independent of the type of roughness, and depends only on turbulence, hence the validity of using the equivalent sand roughness. Substituting the values of κ and ϕ_1 in Eq. (4.39), the law for velocity distribution for completely rough turbulence is

$$\frac{u}{u_*} = 2{\cdot}5\,ln\left(\frac{y}{k_s}\right) + 8{\cdot}5 \tag{4.40}$$

It is interesting to note that Eq. (4.37), when written as

$$\frac{u}{u_*} = \frac{1}{\kappa}ln\left(\frac{u_*y}{\upsilon}\right) - \frac{1}{\kappa}ln\left(\frac{u_*k_s}{\upsilon}\right) + \frac{u_0}{u_*} - \frac{1}{\kappa}ln\,\varepsilon$$

and the condition of hydraulic smoothness, $\varepsilon = 1$ and $k_s = y_0$ is applied, the equation reduces to Eq. (4.25).

4.7 Mean velocity in turbulent flow

The procedure for the derivation of mean velocity of flow from the law of velocity distribution is as follows:

(a) Take an element of area dA within the cross section of the channel, so that its distance from the solid boundary is constant.

(b) Read the velocity distribution law, and the expressions for u and dA into the equation

$$AU = \int_A u\,dA \tag{4.41}$$

and evaluate the integral. For turbulent flow, it simplifies the algebra by working out the expression for the velocity at the point of zero shear before performing the integration. This velocity, denoted by U_0, is the theoretical maximum found anywhere in the cross section. It occurs at the centre line of a full-flowing pipe, and in the free surface of an open channel.

As a simple illustration of the procedure, recall the well-known Hagen-Poisseuille parabolic law of velocity distribution in laminar flow in a thin circular tube carrying a fluid under pressure. Here,

$$u = \frac{1}{4\mu}(2ay - y^2)\frac{dp}{dx} \tag{4.42}$$

where a is the inside radius of the tube (Fig. 4.4), and p the pressure acting on the fluid. By taking

$$dA = 2\pi(a - y)dy \tag{4.43}$$

the procedure gives

$$U = -\frac{1}{8\mu} a^2 \frac{dp}{dx} \tag{4.44}$$

The maximum velocity occurs at the centre of the pipe, and its magnitude U_0 is given by

$$U_0 = -\frac{1}{4\mu} a^2 \frac{dp}{dx} \tag{4.45}$$

From Eqs (4.44) and (4.45) it can be inferred that, due to the parabolic law of velocity distribution, the mean velocity of laminar flow in a thin tube is half of the maximum velocity.

The following paragraphs determine the mean velocity in channels of various shapes.

4.7.1 Smooth circular pipe

Let a circular pipe of radius a be running just full (absolute pressure = 1·0 bar). Take an elementary annulus of depth dy, at a distance y from the wall (Fig. 4.4).

From Eq. (4.35), the velocity U_0 at the centre line of the pipe is given by

$$\frac{U_0}{u_*} = 2 \cdot 5 \ln\left(\frac{u_* a}{v}\right) + 5 \cdot 5 \tag{4.46}$$

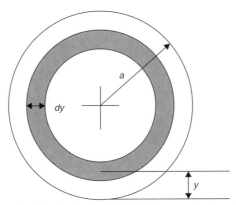

Figure 4.4 *Cross section for the determination of mean velocity of flow in a circular pipe running full.*

Subtracting Eq. (4.46) from Eq. (4.35)

$$\frac{u}{u_*} = \frac{U_0}{u_*} + 2 \cdot 5 \ln\left(\frac{y}{a}\right)$$

(4.47)

The substitution of this expression for u/u_*, and for dA from Eq. (4.43), into Eq. (4.41) gives

$$\pi a^2 \frac{U}{u_*} = \int_0^a \left(\frac{U_0}{u_*} + 2 \cdot 5 \ln\frac{y}{a}\right)[2\pi(a-y)]dy$$

that is,

$$a^2 \frac{U}{u_*} = 2\int_0^a \frac{U_0}{u_*}(a-y)dy + 5\int_0^a (a-y)\ln\frac{y}{a}dy$$

$$= \frac{U_0}{u_*}a^2 + 5\int_0^a a \ln\frac{y}{a}dy - 5\int_0^a y \ln\frac{y}{a}dy$$

With the values of the integrals

$$\int_0^a \ln\frac{y}{a}dy = -a$$

and

$$\int_0^a y \ln\frac{y}{a}dy = -\frac{1}{4}a^2$$

we have

$$a^2 \frac{U}{u_*} = \frac{U_0}{u_*}a^2 - 5a^2 + 1 \cdot 25a^2$$

that is,

$$\frac{U}{u_*} = \frac{U_0}{u_*} - 3 \cdot 75$$

(4.48)

The elimination of U_0 between Eqs (4.46) and (4.48) gives

$$\frac{U}{u_*} = 2 \cdot 5 \ln\left(\frac{u_* a}{v}\right) + 1 \cdot 75$$

(4.49)

4.7.2 Rough circular pipe

Since the difference between the numerical values in Eq. (4.35) for smooth turbulence, and Eq. (4.40) for rough turbulence is only in the free term, and Eq. (4.47) applies to both rough and smooth pipes, the expressions for the maximum velocity U_0, and the mean velocity U, in a rough circular pipe can be written by adjusting the free term in accordance with Eqs (4.46) and (4.49), respectively. In this way, we obtain

$$\frac{U_0}{u_*} = 2 \cdot 5 \, ln\left(\frac{a}{k_s}\right) + 8 \cdot 5 \qquad (4.50)$$

and

$$\frac{U}{u_*} = 2 \cdot 5 \, ln\left(\frac{a}{k_s}\right) + 4 \cdot 75 \qquad (4.51)$$

Example 4.1: A smooth circular pipe, 500 mm diameter, is laid at a gradient (S_0) of 1:100 for transporting water. If the kinematic viscosity of water is $1 \cdot 13 \times 10^{-6} \, m^2/s$, find maximum and mean velocities of flow.

Solution:

$$a = d/2 = 0 \cdot 25 \, m$$

$$R = d/4 = 0 \cdot 125 \, m$$

$$u_* = \sqrt{gRS_0} = \sqrt{9 \cdot 806 \, (0 \cdot 125)(0 \cdot 01)} = 0 \cdot 1107 \, m/s$$

From Eq. (4.46)

$$\frac{U_0}{u_*} = 2 \cdot 5 \, ln\left[\frac{(0 \cdot 1107)(0 \cdot 25) \times 10^6}{1 \cdot 13}\right] + 5 \cdot 5 = 25 \cdot 265 + 5 \cdot 5 = 30 \cdot 765$$

Hence,

$$U_0 = 30 \cdot 765 \times 0 \cdot 1107 = 3 \cdot 406 \, m/s$$

From Eq. (4.48)

$$\frac{U}{u_*} = 30 \cdot 765 - 3 \cdot 75 = 27 \cdot 015$$

Therefore,

$$U = 27 \cdot 015 \times 0 \cdot 1107 = 2 \cdot 99 \, m/s$$

The same value is obtained if Eq. (4.49) is used.

We find that the ratio of mean to maximum velocity in turbulent flow in a pipe is 0·88. This is typically much higher than if the flow were laminar. As shown for laminar flow, the ratio is 0·5.

Example 4.2: If the pipe in Example 4.1 is rough, with the height of equivalent sand roughness $k_s = 1·0\,$mm, find the maximum and mean velocities of flow.

Solution:

From Eq. (4.50)

$$\frac{U_0}{u_*} = 2·5\,ln\left[\frac{0·25}{0·001}\right] + 8·5 = 13·804 + 8·5 = 22·304$$

Hence,

$$U_0 = 22·304 \times 0·1107 = 2·469\,\text{m/s}$$

From Eq. (4.51)

$$\frac{U}{u_*} = 22·304 - 3·75 = 18·554$$

Hence,

$$U = 18·554 \times 0·1107 = 2·05\,\text{m/s}$$

4.7.3 Infinitely wide rectangular channel

Let the side walls of a smooth rectangular channel (Fig. 4.5) be separated by a width B, which is large in comparison to h, the height of the free surface of water. Take an elementary strip of depth dy, at a height y from the bottom of the channel. This is allowed since, due to the large width of the channel,

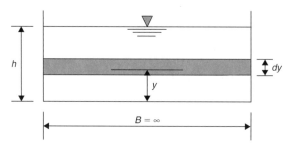

Figure 4.5 *Rectangular cross section of infinite width for the determination of mean velocity of flow.*

the shear between the water and the side walls do not have significant effect on the flow. We now have

$$dA = Bdy \tag{4.52}$$

From Eq. (4.35), the velocity U_0 in the free surface is given by

$$\frac{U_0}{u_*} = 2 \cdot 5 \ln\left(\frac{u_* h}{v}\right) + 5 \cdot 5 \tag{4.53}$$

Following the same steps as in the case of a circular pipe, the following results are obtained:

$$\frac{U}{u_*} = 2 \cdot 5 \ln\left(\frac{u_* h}{v}\right) + 3 \cdot 0 \tag{4.54}$$

The corresponding equations for rough channel are

$$\frac{U_0}{u_*} = 2 \cdot 5 \ln\left(\frac{h}{k_s}\right) + 8 \cdot 5 \tag{4.55}$$

and

$$\frac{U}{u_*} = 2 \cdot 5 \ln\left(\frac{h}{k_s}\right) + 6 \cdot 0 \tag{4.56}$$

In the case of an infinitely wide channel, the depth of flow h, and the hydraulic radius R are of practically the same value.

4.7.4 *Channels of arbitrary shapes*

In treating channels of polygonal, or other shapes, complications arise due to secondary currents around the corners. It has been suggested that these currents are due to two, and in short channels, three-dimensional velocity fluctuations. One of the consequences of this is a non-uniform distribution of shear stress at the wall, and another is the occurrence of the maximum velocity at a distance below the free surface. This distance may vary from 5% to 25% of the depth of flow. The mathematical treatment of channels of arbitrary shapes is highly cumbersome. According to Keulegan [4.7], the 'shape factor' appears as a correction to the free term in Eqs (4.35) and (4.40). In order to evaluate the magnitude of the correction, a rectangular channel of finite width and a triangular channel are considered.

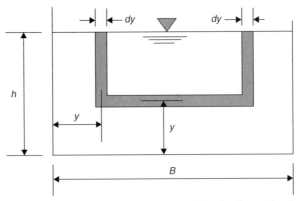

Figure 4.6 *Rectangular cross section of finite width for the determination of mean velocity of flow.*

4.7.5 Rectangular channel of finite width

For a rectangular channel of finite width, take an elementary strip of depth dy as shown in Fig. 4.6. We now have

$$dA = (B - 2y)dy + 2(h - y)dy = (B + 2h - 4y)dy \tag{4.57}$$

From Eq. (4.35), the velocity U_0 in the free surface of flow in a smooth channel is given by

$$\frac{U_0}{u_*} = 2 \cdot 5\,ln\left(\frac{u_* h}{v}\right) + 5 \cdot 5 \tag{4.58}$$

Again, as was done previously, we obtain

$$\frac{U}{u_*} = \frac{U_0}{u_*} - 2 \cdot 5\left(1 + \frac{h}{B}\right) \tag{4.59}$$

that is,

$$\frac{U}{u_*} = 2 \cdot 5\,ln\left(\frac{u_* h}{v}\right) + 5 \cdot 5 - 2 \cdot 5\left(1 + \frac{h}{B}\right) \tag{4.60}$$

If, instead of the depth h, the hydraulic radius R is used, we have instead of Eq. (4.60)

$$\frac{U}{u_*} = 2 \cdot 5\,ln\left(\frac{u_* R}{v}\right) + 5 \cdot 5 - 2 \cdot 5(1 - \beta) \tag{4.61}$$

where

$$\beta = ln\left(\frac{h}{R}\right) - \frac{h}{B} \tag{4.62}$$

The corresponding equations for rough channel are

$$\frac{U_0}{u_*} = 2 \cdot 5 \, ln\left(\frac{h}{k_s}\right) + 8 \cdot 5 \tag{4.63}$$

and

$$\frac{U}{u_*} = 2 \cdot 5 \, ln\left(\frac{h}{k_s}\right) + 8 \cdot 5 - 2 \cdot 5(1 - \beta) \tag{4.64}$$

Example 4.3: A $1 \cdot 2$ m wide rectangular channel is laid at a gradient (S_0) of $0 \cdot 011$ for transporting water. If the maximum depth of water in the channel is $1 \cdot 0$ m, and the kinematic viscosity of water is $1 \cdot 13 \times 10^{-6}$ m²/s, find the mean velocity of flow if the channel is (a) smooth and (b) rough ($k_s = 1 \cdot 0$ mm).

Solution:

(a) *Smooth channel*

$$R = \frac{Bh}{B + 2h} = \frac{1 \cdot 2 \times 1 \cdot 0}{3 \cdot 2} = 0 \cdot 375 \text{ m}$$

$$h/B = 0 \cdot 8333$$

$$h/R = 2 \cdot 6666$$

$$u_* = \sqrt{gRS_0} = \sqrt{9 \cdot 806 \, (0 \cdot 375)(0 \cdot 011)} = 0 \cdot 201 \text{ m/s}$$

From Eq. (4.58)

$$\frac{U_0}{u_*} = 2 \cdot 5 \, ln\left[\frac{(0 \cdot 201)(1 \cdot 0) \times 10^6}{1 \cdot 13}\right] + 5 \cdot 5 = 30 \cdot 222 + 5 \cdot 5 = 35 \cdot 722$$

Therefore,

$$U_0 = 35 \cdot 722 \times 0 \cdot 201 = 7 \cdot 18 \text{ m/s}$$

From Eq. (4.62)

$$\beta = ln(2 \cdot 6666) - 0 \cdot 8333 = 0 \cdot 1475$$

From Eq. (4.61)

$$\frac{U}{u_*} = 2 \cdot 5 \, ln \left[\frac{(0 \cdot 201)(0 \cdot 375) \times 10^6}{1 \cdot 13} \right] + 5 \cdot 5 - 2 \cdot 5 (1 - 0 \cdot 1475)$$

$$= 27 \cdot 770 + 5 \cdot 5 - 2 \cdot 131 = 31 \cdot 139$$

Therefore,

$$U = 0 \cdot 201 \times 31 \cdot 139 = 6 \cdot 259 \, \text{m/s}$$

(b) Rough channel
From Eq. (4.66)

$$\frac{U}{u_*} = 2 \cdot 5 \, ln \left[\frac{1 \cdot 0}{0 \cdot 001} \right] + 8 \cdot 5 - 2 \cdot 5 (1 - 0 \cdot 1475)$$

$$= 17 \cdot 269 + 8 \cdot 5 - 2 \cdot 131 = 23 \cdot 638$$

Therefore,

$$U = 0 \cdot 201 \times 23 \cdot 638 = 4 \cdot 751 \, \text{m/s}$$

4.7.6   Triangular channel

Consider a triangular channel with the cross section shown in Fig. 4.7. Following the procedure given in reference [4.7], let the bisector of the angle at the bottom of the channel intersect the free surface at the point O, and let Y, the perpendicular distance from O to either side of the channel represent the depth of water h. Taking an elementary strip (chevron) of depth dy as shown, we have

$$p_1 = \text{length AB} = \lambda_1(Y - y) \tag{4.65}$$

$$p_2 = \text{length AC} = \lambda_2(Y - y) \tag{4.66}$$

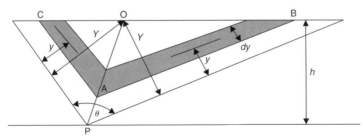

Figure 4.7 *Triangular cross section for the determination of mean velocity of flow.*

and the wetted perimeter

$$P = (\lambda_1 + \lambda_2)Y \tag{4.67}$$

where

$$\lambda_1 = \cot(\theta/2) + \cot\alpha_1$$

$$\lambda_2 = \cot(\theta/2) + \cot\alpha_2$$

The area dA of the elementary strip is given by

$$dA = (p_1 + p_2)dy = (\lambda_1 + \lambda_2)(Y - y)$$

which gives on integrating

$$A = \int_0^Y dA = \frac{1}{2}(\lambda_1 + \lambda_2)Y^2 \tag{4.68}$$

and

$$R = \frac{A}{P} = \frac{Y}{2} \tag{4.69}$$

From Eq. (4.35), the velocity U_0 at C is given by

$$\frac{U_0}{u_*} = 2 \cdot 5 \, ln\left(\frac{u_* Y}{v}\right) + 5 \cdot 5 \tag{4.70}$$

Hence, we obtain through Eqs (4.41) and (4.47) and after replacing a by Y.

$$A \frac{U}{u_*} = \int_0^Y \left(\frac{U_0}{u_*} + 2 \cdot 5 \, ln \frac{y}{Y}\right) dA$$

After the integral has been worked out, the result is

$$\frac{U}{u_*} = \frac{U_0}{u_*} - 3 \cdot 75 \tag{4.71}$$

The combination of this equation with Eq. (4.70) gives

$$\frac{U}{u_*} = 2 \cdot 5 \, ln\left(\frac{u_* Y}{v}\right) + 5 \cdot 5 - 3 \cdot 75 \tag{4.72}$$

If, instead of Y, the hydraulic radius R is used, then we have, instead of Eq. (4.72),

$$\frac{U}{u_*} = 2 \cdot 5 \, ln\left(\frac{u_* R}{v}\right) + 5 \cdot 5 - 2 \cdot 5(1 - \beta) \tag{4.73}$$

where

$$\beta = ln\left(\frac{Y}{R}\right) - 0 \cdot 5 = ln\, 2 - 0 \cdot 5 = 0 \cdot 193 \tag{4.74}$$

It is interesting to note that the correction β for a triangular channel is independent of the dimensions of the cross section. Hence, we have

$$\frac{U}{u_*} = 2 \cdot 5 \, ln\left(\frac{u_* R}{v}\right) + 3 \cdot 48 \tag{4.75}$$

The corresponding equations for a rough channel are

$$\frac{U_0}{u_*} = 2 \cdot 5 \, ln\left(\frac{R}{k_s}\right) + 8 \cdot 5 + ln\, 2$$

that is,

$$\frac{U_0}{u_*} = 2 \cdot 5 \, ln\left(\frac{R}{k_s}\right) + 9 \cdot 19 \tag{4.76}$$

and

$$\frac{U}{u_*} = 2 \cdot 5 \, ln\left(\frac{R}{k_s}\right) + 8 \cdot 5 - 2 \cdot 5(1 - 0 \cdot 193)$$

that is,

$$\frac{U}{u_*} = 2 \cdot 5 \, ln\left(\frac{R}{k_s}\right) + 6 \cdot 48 \tag{4.77}$$

Example 4.4: A 500 mm wide triangular channel (Fig. 4.8) is laid at a gradient (S_0) of 1:110 for transporting water. If the channel runs up to its full

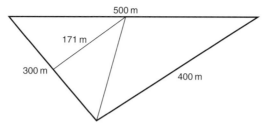

Figure 4.8 *Triangular channel.*

capacity, find the mean velocity of flow if the channel is (*a*) smooth and (*b*) rough ($k_s = 1 \cdot 0$ mm). The kinematic viscosity of water is $1 \cdot 13 \times 10^{-6}$ m²/s.

Solution:

(*a*) *Smooth channel*

$$A = 0 \cdot 06 \text{ m}^2$$

$$P = 0 \cdot 7 \text{ m}$$

$$R = A/P = 0 \cdot 0857 \text{ m}$$

$$u_* = \sqrt{gRS_0} = \sqrt{9 \cdot 806 \, (0 \cdot 0857)/110} = 0 \cdot 0874 \text{ m/s}$$

From Eq. (4.75)

$$\frac{U}{u_*} = 2 \cdot 5 \, ln\left[\frac{(0 \cdot 0874)(0 \cdot 0857) \times 10^6}{1 \cdot 13}\right] + 3 \cdot 48 = 22 \cdot 0 + 3 \cdot 48 = 25 \cdot 48$$

Therefore,

$$U = 0 \cdot 0874 \times 25 \cdot 48 = 2 \cdot 23 \text{ m/s}$$

(*b*) *Rough channel*
From Eq. (4.77)

$$\frac{U}{u_*} = 2 \cdot 5 \, ln\left[\frac{0 \cdot 0857}{0 \cdot 001}\right] + 6 \cdot 48 = 11 \cdot 13 + 6 \cdot 48 = 17 \cdot 61$$

Therefore,

$$U = 0 \cdot 0874 \times 17 \cdot 61 = 1 \cdot 54 \text{ m/s}$$

The case of a trapezoidal channel, which has the cross section in the shape of a half regular hexagon (Fig. 4.9), can be treated similarly.

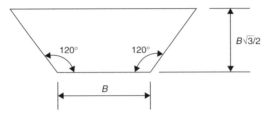

Figure 4.9 *A trapezoidal channel of cross section half regular hexagon.*

Table 4.1 *Free term in the velocity-distribution law*

Channel geometry	Variable	Free term (δ)	
		Smooth	Rough
Circular	$a = 2R$	3·48	6·48
Rectangular (infinite width)	$h = R$	3·0	6·0
Rectangular (finite width)	h	$3·0 + 2·5\beta^*$	$6·0 + 2·5\beta^*$
Triangular	$Y = R^{**}$	3·48	6·48

Note: $^*\beta = \ln(h/R) - (h/B)$; ** for the definition of Y see Fig. 4.7, section 4.7.6.

The result is that the expression for the mean velocity is identical to that for a triangular channel. From this it follows that the expression for the mean velocity of flow in a semicircular channel is also the same, for the cross section can be replaced by a trapezium of infinite-sided regular polygon. The case of a trapezoidal channel of an arbitrary shape has also been discussed in reference [4.7].

4.8   Unification of the laws of mean velocity of flow

For channels, other than circular, it is universal to use the hydraulic radius as the argument of the logarithmic term in the laws of velocity distribution and, since these laws are derived for a circular section, adjust the free term δ. This allows the use of one single expression for the velocity distribution. This is of the form

$$\delta = \delta_0 + 2·5 \ln J_0 \tag{4.78}$$

where δ_0 is the individual free term in the original expression for the mean velocity, δ is the adjusted free term, and J_0 is the ratio of the variable used to the hydraulic radius.

The δ values for various cases, discussed in section 4.7, are given in Table 4.1. It is noticeable that, except for the parameter β, the values of the free term are:

for smooth channel   3·25
for rough channel   6·25

References

[4.1] PRANDTL L., *Essentials of Fluid Dynamics*, Blackie, London, 1957, ch. III.
[4.2] SCHLICHTING H., *Boundary Layer Theory*, translated from German by J. Kestin, McGraw-Hill, New York, 1968, ch. XX.
[4.3] NIKURADSE J., *Gesetzmassigkeit der Turbulenten Stromung in Glatten Rohren*, Forsch. Arb., Ing.-Wes. No. 356, 1932.
[4.4] REICHARDT H., 'Die Warmeubertragung in Turbulenten Reibungsschichten', ZAMM, **20**, 1940, 297–328.
[4.5] BRODKEY R.S., *The Phenomenon of Fluid Motion*, Addison-Wesley, London, 1967, p. 243.
[4.6] NIKURADSE J., *Stromungsgesetze in Rauhen Rohren*, Forsch. Arb., Ing.-Wes. No. 361, 1933.
[4.7] KEULEGAN G.H., 'Laws of Turbulent Flow in Open Channels', National Bureau of Standards, Research Paper RP1151, 1938, 707–741.

5

Laws of resistance to flow

The laws for velocity distribution, covered in Chapter 4, are used in this chapter, which focuses on the development of the laws of resistance to flow. A combination of Darcy-Weisbach law, shear velocity and the velocity distribution law leads to the laws of resistance for turbulence. Initially the derivation pertains to the extreme cases of perfectly smooth turbulence and completely rough turbulence defined in Chapter 4. This is followed by the derivation of the Colbrook-White transitional formula, which is applicable to the turbulence of the intermediate degree. A section is devoted to exact and numerical solutions of the resistance equation with several examples.

5.1 The Darcy-Weisbach law

The most commonly applied resistance law for a pipe flowing full is the Darcy-Weisbach law. In its usual form

$$h_f = f \frac{L}{d} \frac{U^2}{2g} \tag{5.1}$$

the law gives the loss of head h_f over a length L of the pipe of inside diameter d, and carrying a fluid at a mean velocity U. When applied to channel flow, the Darcy-Weisbach law is written in the form

$$\tau_0 = \frac{1}{8} \lambda (\rho U^2) \tag{5.2}$$

where τ_0 is the average wall shear stress, and λ the associated resistance coefficient.

If a uniform flow is assumed, then there is a unique relationship between the resistance coefficients f and λ, and also between, say, λ and the mean velocity of flow. For h_f/L can be replaced by S_0 in Eq. (5.1), and τ_0 by $\gamma R S_0$ in

Eq. (5.2) to obtain

$$U = \sqrt{\frac{2}{f}(gdS_0)} \qquad (5.3)$$

and

$$U = \sqrt{\frac{8}{\lambda}(gRS_0)} \qquad (5.4)$$

The key parameter in these equations is the coefficient of friction λ, which is to be determined by applying the appropriate law of velocity distribution. For a circular pipe, $R = d/4$ which means $\lambda = f$.

As a simple example, recall the mean velocity of flow

$$U = -\frac{1}{8\mu}a^2\frac{dp}{dx} \qquad (4.44)$$

determined from the Hagen-Poisseuille law. The associated maximum (wall) shear stress, obtained by applying the law of viscosity to Eq. (4.42), is

$$\tau_0 = -\frac{1}{2}a\frac{dp}{dx} \qquad (5.5)$$

By eliminating dp/dx between these equations, and adjusting the result, we obtain

$$\tau_0 = \frac{1}{8}\left(\frac{32v}{aU}\right)\rho U^2$$

When compared with Eq. (5.2), this gives

$$\lambda = 32\frac{v}{aU} \qquad (5.6)$$

This is the resistance law relating the coefficient of friction with the mean velocity of flow, and is commonly applied to pipe flow. In terms of the Reynolds number calculated with the diameter as the characteristic length,

$$R = \frac{Ud}{v} \qquad (5.7)$$

the result is

$$\lambda = \frac{64}{R} \tag{5.8}$$

Having established the laws of velocity distribution in smooth and rough turbulence in Chapter 4, let us now proceed to derive the corresponding resistance laws. The procedure adopted here is to follow the conventional line, that is, using the pipe flow as the model to start with, and when the derivation of the law is complete, substituting the hydraulic radius for the pipe diameter that is generally taken as the characteristic linear dimension for calculating the Reynolds number in pipe flow.

5.2 Coefficient of resistance for perfectly smooth turbulence

The earliest form of the relationship between the resistance coefficient and the Reynolds number is the Blasius formula [5.1]:

$$\lambda = \frac{0{\cdot}316}{R^{1/4}} \tag{5.9}$$

This formula was the outcome of a survey of a large amount of experimental data for turbulent flow through smooth pipes, for Reynolds numbers up to 10^5. The subsequent development of the theory of turbulence, and its application to both smooth and rough regimes, led to the determination of the resistance coefficient on a more rational basis, and which could be applied to flows at higher Reynolds numbers. This is discussed in the following paragraphs.

From the relationship between the wall shear stress and the friction velocity (Eq. (4.12)), we obtain

$$\tau_0 = \rho u_*^2 \tag{5.10}$$

The substitution of the expression for τ_0 into the Darcy-Weisbach law (Eq. (5.2)) gives

$$\frac{u_*}{U} = \sqrt{\frac{\lambda}{8}} \tag{5.11}$$

The combination of this and Eq. (4.49):

$$\frac{U}{u_*} = 2{\cdot}5 \, ln\left(\frac{u_* a}{v}\right) + 1{\cdot}75 \tag{4.49}$$

leads to a single equation which is, in effect, the law of resistance for smooth turbulence in circular pipes flowing full. For instance, by rewriting the right-hand side of Eq. (4.49) as

$$2 \cdot 5 \, ln \left(1 \cdot 0069 R \frac{u_*}{U} \right)$$

and eliminating u_*/U between this and Eq. (5.11), we obtain

$$\frac{1}{\sqrt{\lambda}} = 0 \cdot 8839 \, ln(R\sqrt{\lambda}) - 0 \cdot 91$$

or

$$\frac{1}{\sqrt{\lambda}} = 2 \cdot 035 \log(R\sqrt{\lambda}) - 0 \cdot 91 \tag{5.12}$$

The linear relationship between $1/\sqrt{\lambda}$ and $\log(R/\sqrt{\lambda})$, after Stanton and Pannal [5.2], has been verified experimentally by several researchers (see reference [5.3], p. 573), where the best-fit straight line through the data points is represented by the equation

$$\frac{1}{\sqrt{\lambda}} = 2 \cdot 0 \log(R\sqrt{\lambda}) - 0 \cdot 8$$

or

$$\frac{1}{\sqrt{\lambda}} = 2 \cdot 0 \log \left(\frac{R\sqrt{\lambda}}{2 \cdot 51} \right) \tag{5.13}$$

An alternative form of Eq. (5.13) is derived as follows: Recalling Eq. (4.15) for the frictional velocity

$$u_* = \sqrt{gRS_0} \tag{4.15}$$

and eliminating u_* between this and Eq. (5.11), we obtain

$$U = \sqrt{\frac{8gRS_0}{\lambda}} = \sqrt{\frac{2gdS_0}{\lambda}}$$

that is,

$$\frac{1}{\sqrt{\lambda}} = \frac{U}{\sqrt{2gdS_0}} \tag{5.14}$$

The comparison of the right-hand sides of Eqs (5.13) and (5.14) gives

$$U = 2 \cdot 0\sqrt{2gdS_0} \, \log\left(\frac{d\sqrt{2gdS_0}}{2 \cdot 51v}\right) \tag{5.15}$$

Equations (5.14) and (5.15) are accepted as the resistance law for smooth turbulence in a full-flowing circular pipe.

Example 5.1: A 200 mm diameter, 400 m long smooth steel pipe, delivers water for which v is $1 \cdot 13 \times 10^{-6}$ m²/s. If the total head loss is 5 m, calculate the discharge. Assume that the pipe runs just full.

Solution:

$$R = \frac{200 \cdot 0}{4} = 50 \text{ mm}$$

$$S_0 = \frac{h_f}{L} = \frac{5 \cdot 0}{400 \cdot 0} = 0 \cdot 0125$$

$$\sqrt{2gdS_0} = \sqrt{2(9 \cdot 806)(0 \cdot 2)(0 \cdot 0125)} = 0 \cdot 2214 \text{ m/s}$$

From Eq. (5.15)

$$U = 2 \cdot 0\sqrt{2gdS_0} \, \log\left(\frac{d\sqrt{2gdS_0}}{2 \cdot 51v}\right)$$

$$= 2(0 \cdot 2214)\log\left[\frac{(0 \cdot 2)(0 \cdot 2214)}{(2 \cdot 51)(1 \cdot 13) \times 10^{-6}}\right] = 1 \cdot 857 \text{ m/s}$$

$$A = \frac{1}{4}\pi(0 \cdot 04) = 0 \cdot 0314 \text{ m}^2$$

Therefore,

$$Q = (0 \cdot 0314)(1 \cdot 857) \times 1000 = 58 \text{ l/s}$$

5.3 Coefficient of resistance for completely rough turbulence

The derivation of the resistance coefficient for rough turbulence is similar to that which led to Eq. (5.14). Here, U/u_* is eliminated between

Eq. (4.51)

$$\frac{U}{u_*} = 2.5 \ln\left(\frac{a}{k_s}\right) + 4.75 \tag{4.51}$$

and Eq. (5.11) to obtain

$$\frac{1}{\sqrt{\lambda}} = 0.8839 \ln\left(\frac{a}{k_s}\right) + 1.68 \tag{5.16}$$

Results of Nikuradse's experiments on sand-roughened pipes have been accepted as the basis for commercial design of rough pipes and, accordingly, the coefficient of the variable term, and the free term are adjusted to 0.86 and 1.74, respectively. This means that the resistance coefficient is now given by

$$\frac{1}{\sqrt{\lambda}} = 0.86 \ln\left(\frac{a}{k_s}\right) + 1.74$$

or

$$\frac{1}{\sqrt{\lambda}} = 2 \log\left(3.7\frac{d}{k_s}\right) \tag{5.17}$$

The elimination of λ between this and Eq. (5.14) results in the following alternative form of the resistance law:

$$U = 2.0\sqrt{2gdS_0}\log\left(3.7\frac{d}{k_s}\right) \tag{5.18}$$

Example 5.2: A 200 mm diameter, 400 m long rough steel pipe, delivers water. Using the following data, calculate the discharge. Assume that the pipe runs just full.

$h_f = 8.0\,\text{m}$
$k_s = 2.0\,\text{mm}$
$v = 1.13 \times 10^{-6}\,\text{m}^2/\text{s}$

Solution:

$R = d/4 = 0.05\,\text{m}$

$$S_0 = \frac{h_f}{L} = \frac{8.0}{400.0} = 0.02$$

From Eq. (4.15)

$$u_* = \sqrt{gRS_0} = \sqrt{(9 \cdot 806)(0 \cdot 05)(0 \cdot 02)} = 0 \cdot 099 \text{ m/s}$$

From Eq. (4.36)

$$R_k = \frac{u_* k_s}{v} = \frac{(0 \cdot 099)(0 \cdot 002)}{1 \cdot 13 \times 10^{-6}} = 175$$

Since, R_k is >70, this is the case of completely rough turbulence. From Eq. (5.18)

$$U = 2 \cdot 0 \sqrt{2gdS_0} \, \log\left(3 \cdot 7 \frac{d}{k_s}\right)$$

$$= 2\sqrt{2(9 \cdot 806)(0 \cdot 2)(0 \cdot 02)} \, \log\left[3 \cdot 7\left(\frac{0 \cdot 2}{0 \cdot 002}\right)\right] = (0 \cdot 56)(2 \cdot 568)$$

$$= 1 \cdot 438 \text{ m/s}$$

$$A = \frac{1}{4}\pi(0 \cdot 04) = 0 \cdot 0314 \text{ m}^2$$

Therefore,

$$Q = (0 \cdot 0314)(1 \cdot 438) \times 1000 = 45 \, \text{l/s}$$

5.4   Resistance equations for channels of arbitrary shapes

It was assumed in the derivation of the resistance equations that the pipe is flowing full and, therefore, cannot be applied to partially full pipes. In order to apply these equations to such flow conditions, as well as to channels of arbitrary shapes, the common practice is to replace the diameter d by the hydraulic radius $R = d/4$. Hence, we obtain from Eqs (5.11) and (5.15), for smooth turbulence

$$\frac{1}{\sqrt{\lambda}} = \frac{U}{\sqrt{8gRS_0}} \tag{5.19}$$

and

$$U = \sqrt{32gRS_0} \, \log\left(\frac{R\sqrt{32gRS_0}}{1 \cdot 255v}\right) \tag{5.20}$$

Likewise, for completely rough turbulence, we obtain from Eq. (5.18)

$$U = \sqrt{32gRS_0} \; \log\left(14{\cdot}8\frac{R}{k_s}\right) \tag{5.21}$$

Example 5.3: The cross section of a smooth channel, laid at a bed slope of 1:200, has the following section properties: $A = 0{\cdot}144\,\mathrm{m^2}$, $R = 0{\cdot}112\,\mathrm{m}$. If $v = 1{\cdot}141 \times 10^{-6}\,\mathrm{m^2/s}$, calculate (a) the rate of discharge and (b) the resistance coefficient.

Solution:

$$\sqrt{32gRS_0} = \sqrt{32(9{\cdot}806)(0{\cdot}112)(0{\cdot}005)} = 0{\cdot}419\,\mathrm{m/s}$$

(a) From Eq. (5.20)

$$U = \sqrt{32gRS_0} \; \log\left(\frac{R\sqrt{32gRS_0}}{1{\cdot}255v}\right)$$

$$= (0{\cdot}419)\log\left(\frac{(0{\cdot}112)(0{\cdot}419)}{(1{\cdot}255)(1{\cdot}141)\times 10^{-6}}\right) = 1{\cdot}892\,\mathrm{m/s}$$

$$Q = UA = (1{\cdot}892)(0{\cdot}144)(1000) = 272\,\mathrm{l/s}$$

(b) From Eq. (5.19)

$$\sqrt{\lambda} = \frac{\sqrt{8gRS_0}}{U} = \frac{0{\cdot}419}{2(1{\cdot}892)} = 0{\cdot}1107$$

Therefore,

$$\lambda = 0{\cdot}0123$$

Example 5.4: If in Example 5.3, the average height of roughness is $1{\cdot}2\,\mathrm{mm}$, calculate (a) the rate of discharge and (b) the resistance coefficient.

Solution:

From Eq. (4.15)

$$u_* = \sqrt{gRS_0} = \sqrt{(9{\cdot}806)(0{\cdot}112)(0{\cdot}005)} = 0{\cdot}0741\,\mathrm{m/s}$$

From Eq. (4.36)

$$R_k = \frac{u_* k_s}{v} = \frac{(0{\cdot}0741)(0{\cdot}0012)}{1{\cdot}141 \times 10^{-6}} = 78$$

This is the case of completely rough turbulence.

(*a*) From Eq. (5.21)

$$U = \sqrt{32gRS_0}\,\log\left(14{\cdot}8\frac{R}{k_s}\right)$$

$$= 0{\cdot}419\log\left[14{\cdot}8\left(\frac{0{\cdot}112}{0{\cdot}0012}\right)\right] = 1{\cdot}32\ \text{m/s}$$

$$Q = UA = (1{\cdot}32)(0{\cdot}144)(1000) = 190\,\text{l/s}$$

(*b*) From Eq. (5.19)

$$\sqrt{\lambda} = \frac{\sqrt{8gRS_0}}{U} = \frac{0{\cdot}419}{2(1{\cdot}32)} = 0{\cdot}159$$

Therefore,

$$\lambda = 0{\cdot}025$$

5.5 Colebrook-White transition formula

The resistance equations, discussed above, are applicable only to the extreme flow situations, that is, when the roughness Reynolds number is either less than 5 (perfectly smooth turbulence), or greater than 70 (completely rough turbulence). An empirical formula which covers the intermediate levels of roughness, is due to Colebrook [5.4], and is known as the *Colebrook-White transition formula*. Since, in most of flow situations involving commercial pipes and channels, the roughness lies between the limits of smooth and rough turbulence, Colebrook-White formula is accepted as the only formula that can be applied in the design of pipes, and channels of non-circular cross sections. This formula, which may be called the *transition equation*, combines the resistance law for smooth and rough turbulence in such a way that it is applicable also to the limiting situations, that is, when turbulence is either smooth or completely rough. Hence, the transition equation for circular pipes, obtained from Eqs (5.13) and (5.17) is

$$\frac{1}{\sqrt{\lambda}} = -2{\cdot}0\log\left(\frac{2{\cdot}51}{R\sqrt{\lambda}} + \frac{k_s}{3{\cdot}7d}\right) \tag{5.22}$$

The implicit manner in which the resistance coefficient λ occurs in the transition equation restricts its exact solution to the situations in which only

Q is unknown. In other situations, resort is taken to a graphical or numerical method of solution. It is to be emphasized, however, that the resistance equation offers a method of solving a flow problem which tacitly assumes a uniform flow condition.

5.6 Limiting case of rough turbulence

It was mentioned above that when the roughness Reynolds number exceeds 70, the mainstream Reynolds number, at which the flow takes place, has little effect on the resistance to flow and, as a result, the coefficient of resistance depends entirely on the roughness Reynolds number R_k. Rewriting Eq. (4.36) as

$$R_k = \frac{k_s \, u_*}{d \, U} R$$

that is,

$$\frac{k_s}{d} = \frac{R_k}{R} \sqrt{\frac{8}{\lambda}}$$

and eliminating k_s/d between this and Eq. (5.22), we obtain

$$\frac{1}{\sqrt{\lambda}} = -2 \cdot 0 \log \left(\frac{2 \cdot 51}{R \sqrt{\lambda}} + \frac{1}{3 \cdot 7} \sqrt{\frac{8}{\lambda}} \frac{R_k}{R} \right) \tag{5.23}$$

For the case of perfectly smooth turbulence, $R_k = 0$, and the above equation reduces to Eq. (5.13). For the limiting case of rough turbulence, $R_k = 70$, and we have

$$\frac{1}{\sqrt{\lambda}} = -2 \cdot 0 \log \left(\frac{53 \cdot 51}{R \sqrt{\lambda}} \right) \tag{5.24}$$

In most situations of practical interest, the roughness Reynolds number lies within these limits.

5.7 Uniform flow equation, Chezy's and Manning's roughness factors

It was mentioned in section 3.1 that the rational method used to determine the roughness factors C and n in the uniform flow equations is to apply the law of resistance. Thus, eliminating λ between Eqs (5.14) and (5.22), and substituting for the Reynolds number its expression

$$R = \frac{Ud}{v}$$

we obtain the following equation for the velocity of flow:

$$U = -2 \cdot 0\sqrt{2gdS_0} \, \log\left(\frac{2 \cdot 51v}{d\sqrt{2gdS_0}} + \frac{k_s}{3 \cdot 7d} \right) \tag{5.25}$$

By replacing d by $4R$, we obtain the corresponding equation for non-circular cross sections, that is,

$$U = -\sqrt{32gRS_0} \, \log\left(\frac{1 \cdot 255v}{R\sqrt{32gRS_0}} + \frac{k_s}{14 \cdot 8R} \right) \tag{5.26}$$

The last two equations are accepted as the two versions of the resistance equation of the uniform flow theory, and they are widely used in the design of pipes and open channels of arbitrary shapes. They also provide a means of calculating the roughness factors C and n. For instance, comparing Eq. (5.26) with Eq. (3.3)

$$U = C\sqrt{RS_0} \tag{3.3}$$

we deduce the following formula for C:

$$C = -\sqrt{32g} \, \log\left(\frac{1 \cdot 255v}{R\sqrt{32gRS_0}} + \frac{k_s}{14 \cdot 8R} \right) \tag{5.27}$$

The magnitude of Manning's n is then determined from Eq. (3.6)

$$n = \frac{1}{C} R^{1/6} \tag{3.6}$$

An alternative method for calculating Manning's n is to use the Manning-Williamson equation (see reference [5.5]):

$$\lambda = 0 \cdot 18 \left(\frac{k_s}{d} \right)^{1/3} \tag{5.28}$$

By eliminating λ between this equation and the equation

$$\frac{1}{\sqrt{\lambda}} = \frac{U}{\sqrt{2gdS_0}} \tag{5.14}$$

we obtain

$$U = \sqrt{\frac{2gdS_0}{0\cdot18}} \left(\frac{d}{k_s}\right)^{1/6} \tag{5.29}$$

By taking $g = 9\cdot806\,\text{m/s}^2$, and replacing d by $4R$, this equation reduces to

$$U = 26\cdot3\frac{R^{2/3}S_0^{1/2}}{k_s^{1/6}} \tag{5.30}$$

Comparing this with the Manning's formula, Eq. (3.5)

$$U = \frac{1}{n}R^{2/3}S_0^{1/2} \tag{3.5}$$

we obtain

$$n = \frac{k_s^{1/6}}{26\cdot3} \tag{5.31}$$

Example 5.5: Using the following data for an arbitrary channel, determine Chezy's C and Manning's n, and compare the value of n with that obtained from Eq. (5.31).

$$R = 0\cdot841\,\text{m}$$
$$k_s = 1\cdot5\,\text{mm}$$
$$S_0 = 0\cdot0011$$
$$v = 1\cdot141 \times 10^{-6}\,\text{m}^2/\text{s}$$

Solution:

$$\sqrt{32g} = \sqrt{32(9\cdot806)} = 17\cdot7142\,\text{m}^{1/2}/\text{s}$$

$$\sqrt{32gRS_0} = \sqrt{32(9\cdot806)(0\cdot841)(0\cdot0011)} = 0\cdot5388\,\text{m/s}$$

$$\frac{1\cdot255v}{R\sqrt{32gRS_0}} = \frac{1\cdot255(1\cdot141 \times 10^{-6})}{0\cdot841(0\cdot5388)} = 3\cdot1601 \times 10^{-6}$$

$$\frac{k_s}{14\cdot8R} = \frac{1\cdot5 \times 10^{-3}}{14\cdot8(0\cdot841)} = 120\cdot5129 \times 10^{-6}$$

From Eq. (5.27)

$$C = -\sqrt{32g} \log\left(\frac{1 \cdot 255v}{R\sqrt{32gRS_0}} + \frac{k_s}{14 \cdot 8R}\right)$$

$$= -17 \cdot 7142 \log[(3 \cdot 1601 + 120 \cdot 5129) \times 10^{-6}] = 69 \cdot 2222$$

From Eq. (3.6)

$$n = \frac{1}{C} R^{1/6} = \frac{(0 \cdot 841)^{1/6}}{69 \cdot 2222} = 0 \cdot 014 \, \text{s/m}^{1/3}$$

From Eq. (5.31)

$$n = \frac{k_s^{1/6}}{26 \cdot 3} = \frac{(0 \cdot 0015)^{1/6}}{26 \cdot 3} = 0 \cdot 013 \, \text{s/m}^{1/3}$$

In the solution of channel flow problems, discussed in the subsequent chapters, Manning's n is freely used and, while doing so, it is assumed that its value is either known or obtainable. In precast linear drainage channels, n varies over a relatively short range of $0 \cdot 0011$ to $0 \cdot 0013$.

5.8   Solution of the resistance equation

In a given flow problem, involving a circular pipe or an open channel, it is often required to solve the transition equation to determine one of the three parameters:

(a) Discharge capacity Q.
(b) The head loss h_f in a pipe, or the bed slope S_0 in a channel.
(c) The diameter d of the pipe or the depth of flow y in the channel.

The remaining parameters which appear in the resistance equation, namely, the kinematic viscosity of the fluid and the average height of roughness, are assumed to be known.

Since the resistance coefficient λ occurs both outside and within the argument of the logarithmic function, it is not possible to solve the resistance equation exactly, the exception being the condition in which only the discharge rate is unknown. Hence, if a solution is required for (b) and (c) above, one will have to look for a graphical or numerical procedure. Let us begin with an example of exact solution of Eqs (5.25) and (5.26).

5.9 Exact solution of the resistance equation, determination of Q

Example 5.6: From the following flow data, calculate the rate of discharge for a steel pipe:

$$L = 400\,\text{m}$$
$$h_f = 2\cdot0\,\text{m}$$
$$d = 200\,\text{mm}$$
$$k_s = 0\cdot25\,\text{mm}$$
$$v = 1\cdot1 \times 10^{-6}\,\text{m}^2/\text{s}$$

Solution:

$$R = \frac{d}{4} = 50\,\text{mm}$$

$$S_0 = \frac{h_f}{L} = \frac{2.0}{400\cdot0} = 0\cdot005$$

$$\sqrt{2gdS_0} = \sqrt{2(9\cdot806)(0\cdot2)(0\cdot005)} = 0\cdot14\,\text{m/s}$$

$$\frac{2\cdot51v}{d\sqrt{2gdS_0}} = \frac{(2\cdot51)(1\cdot1 \times 10^{-6})}{(0\cdot2)(0\cdot14)} = 98\cdot61 \times 10^{-6}$$

$$\frac{k_s}{3\cdot7d} = \frac{0\cdot00025}{(3\cdot7)(0\cdot2)} = 337\cdot84 \times 10^{-6}$$

$$\log\left(\frac{2.51v}{d\sqrt{2gdS_0}} + \frac{k_s}{3\cdot7d}\right) = \log(98\cdot61 + 337\cdot84) - 6 = -3\cdot36$$

From Eq. (5.25)

$$U = -2\cdot0\sqrt{2gdS_0}\,\log\left(\frac{2\cdot51v}{d\sqrt{2gdS_0}} + \frac{k_s}{3\cdot7d}\right)$$

$$= 2(0\cdot14)(3\cdot36) = 0\cdot94\,\text{m/s}$$

Therefore,

$$Q = UA = 0\cdot94\pi(0\cdot01)(1000) = 29\cdot56\,\text{l/s}$$

Example 5.7: A trapezoidal channel of base width $2 \cdot 0\,\text{m}$ and side slopes of 1:1, is laid at a bed slope of 1:1000. Calculate the rate of discharge, using the following data:

$$B = 2 \cdot 0\,\text{m}$$
$$y = 1 \cdot 5\,\text{m}$$
$$k_s = 1 \cdot 5\,\text{mm}$$
$$v = 1 \cdot 141 \times 10^{-6}\,\text{m}^2/\text{s}$$

Solution:

From the dimensions of the cross section, we determine

$$A = [B + 0 \cdot 5(m_1 + m_2)y]y = 0 \cdot 5(2 \cdot 0 + 1 \cdot 5)(1 \cdot 5) = 5 \cdot 25\,\text{m}^2$$

$$P = B + \left(\sqrt{1 + m_1^2} + \sqrt{1 + m_1^2} \right)y = 2 \cdot 0 + 3 \cdot 0\sqrt{2} = 6 \cdot 243\,\text{m}$$

$$R = \frac{A}{P} = \frac{5 \cdot 25}{6 \cdot 243} = 0 \cdot 841\,\text{m}$$

$$\sqrt{32 g R S_0} = \sqrt{(32)(9 \cdot 806)(0 \cdot 841)(0 \cdot 001)} = 0 \cdot 5137$$

From Eq. (5.26)

$$U = -\sqrt{32 g R S_0}\,\log\left(\frac{1 \cdot 255 v}{R\sqrt{32 g R S_0}} + \frac{k_s}{14 \cdot 8R} \right)$$

$$= -0 \cdot 5137 \log\left[\frac{(1 \cdot 255)(1 \cdot 141 \times 10^{-6})}{(0 \cdot 841)(0 \cdot 5137)} + \frac{0 \cdot 0015}{(14 \cdot 8)(0 \cdot 841)} \right]$$

$$= -0 \cdot 5137 \log(3 \cdot 315 \times 10^{-6} + 120 \cdot 527 \times 10^{-6}) = 2 \cdot 007\,\text{m/s}$$

$$Q = (5 \cdot 25)(2 \cdot 007) = 10 \cdot 537\,\text{m}^3/\text{s}$$

5.10 Graphical method of solution of the resistance equation

A graphical method of solution of the resistance equation was first proposed by Moody [5.6]. Since the equation relates the resistance coefficient λ with two independent variables, the Reynolds number R, and the relative roughness k_s/d, a graphical representation of the relationship is possible only by treating the two variables separately. Hence, the Moody diagram, as it is called, is a chart that consists of several graphs between λ and R, each corresponding to a particular value of k_s/d. The method is essentially applicable to design of pipes, and can best be applied when the diameter of the pipe is known.

Another graphical solution, for wider application of the Colebrook-White equation, was published in 1958 by the Hydraulic Research Laboratory [5.7]. It is in the form of a series of charts showing diameter, velocity and gradient plotted against the average height of roughness k_s. Recently, the same method of solution was presented in tabular form in reference [5.8].

5.11 Numerical solution of the resistance equation

For the numerical solution of the resistance equation, the problems are divided into two groups. In the first group are the problems in which the head loss in a pipe, or the gradient of a channel bed are to be determined. The determination of the pipe diameter or the depth of flow in a channel are the problems of the second group. In any instance, it will be necessary to recast the equation in a form appropriate for solving for the undetermined parameter.

5.11.1 Head loss in a circular pipe

The procedure for the determination of the head loss in a full-flowing pipe consists of solving Eq. (5.22) for λ, and applying the Darcy-Weisbach resistance law. Making the substitution

$$\phi = \frac{1}{\sqrt{\lambda}} \tag{5.32}$$

in Eq. (5.22), and adjusting the terms, we obtain the following two versions of the transition equation

$$\frac{1}{\sqrt{\lambda}} = -2 \cdot 0 \log\left(\frac{2 \cdot 51}{R\sqrt{\lambda}} + \frac{k_s}{3 \cdot 7 d}\right) \tag{5.22}$$

$$F(\phi) = 2\log(\phi + A_1) + \phi + A_2 = 0 \tag{5.33}$$

and

$$F(\phi) = 2\log(A_3\phi + 1) + \phi + A_4 = 0 \tag{5.34}$$

where

$$A_1 = \frac{R}{9 \cdot 287} \frac{k_s}{d} \tag{5.35}$$

$$A_2 = 2\log\left(\frac{2\cdot51}{R}\right) \tag{5.36}$$

$$A_3 = \frac{1}{A_1} \tag{5.37}$$

$$A_4 = 2\log\left(\frac{k_s}{3\cdot7d}\right) \tag{5.38}$$

Suppressing the logarithmic term, an initial trial value of ϕ is taken as the average value of ϕ obtained from Eqs (5.33) and (5.34), that is,

$$\phi_0 = -\frac{1}{2}(A_2 + A_4) = \log\left(1\cdot474R\frac{d}{k_s}\right) \tag{5.39}$$

This value of ϕ can be improved to an initial desired accuracy by applying the Newton-Raphson method (see Appendix A).

Example 5.8: Determine the loss of head over 400 m length of a cast-iron pipe from the following flow data:

$\quad d = 250\,\text{mm}$
$\quad k_s = 0\cdot25\,\text{mm}$
$\quad Q = 200\,\text{l/s}$
$\quad v = 1\cdot0 \times 10^{-5}\,\text{m}^2/\text{s}$

Solution:

$$A = \frac{\pi}{4}(0\cdot25)^2 = 0\cdot0491\,\text{m}^2$$

$$U = \frac{0\cdot2}{0049} = 4\cdot074\,\text{m/s}$$

$$R = (4\cdot074)(0\cdot25) \times 10^5 = 1\cdot02 \times 10^5$$

From Eq. (5.35)

$$A_1 = \frac{R}{9\cdot287}\frac{k_s}{d} = \frac{1\cdot02 \times 10^5}{9\cdot287}\frac{0\cdot00025}{0\cdot25} = 10\cdot983$$

From Eq. (5.36)

$$A_2 = 2\log\left(\frac{2\cdot51}{R}\right) = 2\log\left(\frac{2\cdot51}{1\cdot02 \times 10^5}\right) = -9\cdot218$$

From Eq. (5.39)

$$\phi_0 = \log\left(1\cdot474R\frac{d}{k_s}\right) = \log\left(1\cdot474 \times 1\cdot02 \times 10^5 \times \frac{250}{0\cdot25}\right) = 8\cdot177$$

Applying the Newton-Raphson method (for details see Appendix A, section A.2), we find that values of ϕ after first two iterations are

$$\phi_1 = 6\cdot797 \qquad \phi_2 = 6\cdot726$$

Accepting ϕ_2 as sufficiently accurate to be used as ϕ, we obtain from Eq. (5.32)

$$\lambda = \frac{1}{\phi^2} = 0\cdot0221$$

Therefore,

$$h_f = \lambda\frac{L}{d}\frac{U^2}{2g} = (0\cdot0221)\frac{400}{0\cdot25}\frac{(4\cdot074)^2}{2(9\cdot806)} = 29\cdot9 \text{ m}$$

From the Moody diagram [5.9], for $k_s/d = 0\cdot25/250 = 0\cdot001$, and $R = 1\cdot02 \times 10^5$, we find $\lambda = 0\cdot022$.

5.11.2 Gradient of a channel bed

The equation required to be solved is

$$U = -\sqrt{32gRS_0} \, \log\left(\frac{1\cdot255v}{R\sqrt{32gRS_0}} + \frac{k_s}{14\cdot8R}\right) \tag{5.26}$$

in which we make the following substitution

$$\psi = \frac{1}{\sqrt{S_0}} \tag{5.40}$$

Adjusting the terms, we obtain the following two versions of Eq. (5.26):

$$F(\psi) = \frac{\sqrt{32gR}}{U}\log(\psi + B_1) + \psi + B_2 = 0 \tag{5.41}$$

and

$$F(\psi) = \frac{\sqrt{32gR}}{U}\log(B_3\psi + 1) + \psi + B_4 = 0 \tag{5.42}$$

where

$$B_1 = \frac{k\sqrt{32gR}}{18\cdot57v} \tag{5.43}$$

$$B_2 = \frac{\sqrt{32gR}}{U} \log\left(\frac{1\cdot255v}{R\sqrt{32gR}}\right) \tag{5.44}$$

$$B_3 = \frac{1}{B_1} \tag{5.45}$$

$$B_4 = \frac{\sqrt{32gR}}{U} \log\left(\frac{1}{14\cdot8}\frac{k_s}{R}\right)$$

A trial value of ψ suggested by Eqs (5.41) and (5.42) is

$$\psi_0 = -\frac{1}{2}(B_2 + B_4)$$

that is,

$$\psi_0 = \frac{\sqrt{32gR}}{2U} \log\left(\frac{11\cdot7928R^2\sqrt{32gR}}{kv}\right) \tag{5.46}$$

Example 5.9: Calculate the bed slope to maintain a discharge rate of $11\cdot0\,\text{m}^3/\text{s}$, for a trapezoidal channel with the following data:

$$B = 2\cdot0\,\text{m}$$
$$y = 1\cdot5\,\text{m}$$
$$m_1 = m_2 = 1\cdot0$$
$$k_s = 1\cdot5\,\text{mm}$$
$$v = 1\cdot141 \times 10^{-6}\,\text{m}^2/\text{s}$$

Solution:

$$A = 5\cdot25\,\text{m}^2$$

$$R = 0\cdot841\,\text{m}$$

$$U = \frac{11\cdot0}{5\cdot25} = 2\cdot0952\,\text{m/s}$$

$$\sqrt{32gR} = \sqrt{(32)(9 \cdot 806)(0 \cdot 841)} = 16 \cdot 2450 \text{ m/s}$$

$$\frac{\sqrt{32gR}}{U} = \frac{16 \cdot 2450}{2 \cdot 0952} = 7 \cdot 7534$$

From Eq. (5.43)

$$B_1 = \frac{k\sqrt{32gR}}{18 \cdot 574v} = \frac{(0 \cdot 0015)(16 \cdot 245)}{(18 \cdot 574)(1 \cdot 141 \times 10^{-6})} = 1149 \cdot 79$$

From Eq. (5.44)

$$B_2 = \frac{\sqrt{32gR}}{U} \log\left(\frac{1 \cdot 255v}{R\sqrt{32gR}}\right)$$

$$= 7 \cdot 7534 \log\left[\frac{(1 \cdot 255)(1 \cdot 141 \times 10^{-6})}{(0 \cdot 841)(16 \cdot 245)}\right] = -54 \cdot 115$$

From Eq. (5.46)

$$\psi_0 = \frac{1}{2}(7 \cdot 7534) \log\left|\frac{(11 \cdot 7928)(0 \cdot 841^2)(16 \cdot 245)}{(0 \cdot 0015)(1 \cdot 141 \times 10^{-6})}\right| = 42 \cdot 25$$

When the Newton-Raphson method is applied to improve this value, the solution converges to $\psi = 30 \cdot 3$ (see Appendix A, section A.3). From this we determine

$$S_0 = \frac{1}{\psi^2} = 0 \cdot 0011$$

In order to examine the accuracy of the solution, we substitute the computed value of $\psi = 30 \cdot 3$, in Eq. (5.41), and find the expression on the right-hand side reduces to $0 \cdot 0028$, which is considered as a small tolerance.

5.11.3 Diameter of a pipe

From the relationships

$$U = \frac{4Q}{\pi d^2} \tag{5.47}$$

$$R = \frac{4Q}{\pi d v} \qquad (5.48)$$

$$\lambda = \frac{h_f}{L} \frac{2gd}{U^2} \qquad (5.49)$$

we construct the following equations

$$\frac{1}{\sqrt{\lambda}} = C_1 d^{-5/2} \qquad (5.50)$$

$$\frac{1}{R\sqrt{\lambda}} = C_2 d^{-3/2} \qquad (5.51)$$

where

$$C_1 = \frac{Q}{\pi} \sqrt{\frac{8L}{h_f g}} \qquad (5.52)$$

$$C_2 = v \sqrt{\frac{L}{2h_f g}} \qquad (5.53)$$

Eliminating R and λ between Eqs (5.50), (5.51) and (5.22)

$$\frac{1}{\sqrt{\lambda}} = -2.0 \log\left(\frac{2.51}{R\sqrt{\lambda}} + \frac{k_s}{3.7d} \right) \qquad (5.22)$$

we obtain the following equation in d:

$$\frac{C_1}{d^{5/2}} = -2\log\left(\frac{2.51 C_2}{d^{3/2}} + \frac{k_s}{3.7d} \right)$$

that is,

$$F(d) = 2\log(1 + C_3 d^{1/2}) - 3\log d + C_1 d^{-5/2} + C_4 = 0 \qquad (5.54)$$

where

$$C_3 = \frac{k_s}{9.287 C_2} \qquad (5.55)$$

$$C_4 = 2\log(2.51 C_2) \qquad (5.56)$$

A trial value of d is given by

$$d_0 = \left(-\frac{C_1}{C_4}\right)^{2/5} \tag{5.57}$$

This value of d can be modified by applying the Newton-Raphson method, for which

$$F'(d) = \frac{C_3}{(1 + C_3 d^{1/2})d^{1/2}} - \frac{3}{d} - \frac{5}{2}C_1 d^{-7/2} \tag{5.58}$$

Example 5.10: A wrought iron pipe is to transport oil at the rate of $400\,l/s$. If the head loss over $4000\,m$ length is $40\,m$, determine the size of the pipe from the following data:

$$k_s = 0{\cdot}045\,mm$$
$$v = 1{\cdot}0 \times 10^{-5}\,m^2/s$$

Solution:

From Eq. (5.52)

$$C_1 = \frac{Q}{\pi}\sqrt{\frac{8L}{h_f g}} = \frac{0{\cdot}4}{\pi}\sqrt{\frac{8(4000)}{40(9{\cdot}806)}} = 1{\cdot}15$$

From Eq. (5.53)

$$C_2 = v\sqrt{\frac{L}{2h_f g}}$$

$$= 1{\cdot}0 \times 10^{-5}\sqrt{\frac{4000}{2(40)(9{\cdot}806)}} = 2{\cdot}258 \times 10^{-5}$$

From Eq. (5.55)

$$C_3 = \frac{k_s}{9{\cdot}287 C_2} = \frac{0{\cdot}000045}{9{\cdot}287(2{\cdot}258 \times 10^{-5})} = 0{\cdot}2146$$

From Eq. (5.56)

$$C_4 = 2\log(2{\cdot}51 C_2)$$

$$= 2\log[2{\cdot}51(2{\cdot}258 \times 10^{-5})] = -8{\cdot}4932$$

From Eq. (5.57), the initial trial value of d is given by

$$d_0 = \left(\frac{1\cdot15}{8\cdot4932} \right)^{2/5} = 0\cdot4494 \text{ m}$$

It needs only two trials for the solution to converge to $d = 0\cdot4748$ m, showing that d_0 is within 5% of the exact value.

The nearest (higher) standard diameter available is selected as the required diameter.

The accuracy of the solution is examined by determining U and λ from Eqs (5.47) and (5.50), respectively, and verifying Eq. (5.1) after replacing f by λ. Thus, we have

From Eq. (5.47)

$$U = \frac{4Q}{\pi d^2} = \frac{1\cdot6}{\pi(0\cdot4748^2)} = 2\cdot259 \text{ m/s}$$

From Eq. (5.50)

$$\lambda = \frac{1}{C_1^2} d^5 = \frac{0\cdot4748^5}{1\cdot15^2} = 0\cdot01825$$

From Eq. (5.1)

$$h_f = \lambda \frac{L}{d} \frac{U^2}{2g} = 0\cdot01825 \frac{4000}{0\cdot4748} \frac{2\cdot259^2}{2(9\cdot806)} = 40\cdot0 \text{ m}$$

which agrees with the value specified in the example.

5.11.4 Depth of flow in an open channel

Introducing the notation

$$D_0 = \frac{\sqrt{32 g S_0}}{Q} \tag{5.59}$$

$$D_1 = \frac{k_s \sqrt{32 g S_0}}{18\cdot574 v} \tag{5.60}$$

$$D_2 = D_0 \log \left(\frac{1\cdot255 v}{\sqrt{32 g S_0}} \right) \tag{5.61}$$

Eq. (5.26) can be rewritten as

$$\frac{1}{A\sqrt{R}} = -D_0 \log(1 + D_3 R^{1/2}) + \frac{3}{2} D_0 \log R - D_2 = 0 \tag{5.62}$$

Next, express the area of cross section, the hydraulic radius and the parameter $A\sqrt{R}$ as follows:

$$A = K_1 y^2 \tag{5.63}$$

$$R = K_2 y \tag{5.64}$$

$$A\sqrt{R} = K_3 y^{5/2} \tag{5.65}$$

$$\left[K_3 = K_1 \sqrt{K_2} \right]$$

where the constants K_1, K_2, and K_3 are determined from the geometry of the cross section. When these expressions are substituted into Eq. (5.62), the result is the following equation in y:

$$F(y) = D_0 \log(1 + D_1' R^{1/2}) + \frac{1}{K_3 y^{5/2}} - \frac{3}{2} D_0 \log y + D_1' = 0 \tag{5.66}$$

where

$$D_1' = D_1 \sqrt{K_2} \tag{5.67}$$

$$D_2' = D_2 - \frac{3}{2} D_0 \log K_2 \tag{5.68}$$

Similar to the numerical solution of Eq. (5.54), we start with the following trial value y_0 of y:

$$y_0 = \left(-\frac{1}{K_3 D_2'} \right)^{2/5} \tag{5.69}$$

and improve it by applying the Newton-Raphson method.

Example 5.11: A rectangular channel of width 2 m is laid at a bed slope of 1:1000, and carries a discharge at 15 m³/s. If $k_s = 1 \cdot 5$ mm, and $v = 12 \cdot 5 \times 10^{-6}$ m²/s calculate the depth of flow.
From Eqs (5.59), (5.60) and (5.61), we determine

$$D_0 = 0 \cdot 0373 \qquad D_1 = 3 \cdot 6191 \qquad D_2 = -0 \cdot 17$$

Assuming an initial value of the ratio $B/y = 1{\cdot}0$, the following can be obtained from Eqs (5.63), (5.64), (5.65), (5.67) and (5.68):

$$k_1 = 1{\cdot}0 \qquad k_2 = 0{\cdot}333 \qquad k_3 = 0{\cdot}577$$
$$D_1' = 2{\cdot}0895 \qquad D_2' = -0{\cdot}1433$$

The values of k_3, and D_2' give a starting value y_0 for y from Eq. (5.69) to solve Eq. (5.66). The converged value of y corresponding to the above set of parameters k_1, k_2, k_3, D_1' and D_2' is $2{\cdot}7092\,\text{m}$. These parameters are then modified, and the solution of Eq. (5.66) repeated. After a few iterations we obtain $y = 3{\cdot}961\,\text{m}$.

The accuracy of the solution is verified by calculating the discharge rate. We now have

$$y = 3{\cdot}961\,\text{m}$$

$$P = 2{\cdot}0 + 7{\cdot}922 = 9{\cdot}922\,\text{m}$$

$$A = 7{\cdot}922\,\text{m}^2$$

$$R = A/P = 0{\cdot}7984\,\text{m}$$

$$\frac{k_s}{14{\cdot}8R} = \frac{0{\cdot}0015}{14{\cdot}8 \times 0{\cdot}7984} = 126{\cdot}943 \times 10^{-6}$$

$$\frac{1{\cdot}255v}{R\sqrt{32gRS_0}} = \frac{1{\cdot}255 \times 12{\cdot}5 \times 10^{-6}}{0{\cdot}7984\sqrt{32 \times 9{\cdot}806 \times 0{\cdot}7984 \times 0{\cdot}001}}$$

$$= 39{\cdot}256 \times 10^{-6}$$

From Eq. (5.27)

$$C = -\sqrt{32g}\,\log\left(\frac{1{\cdot}255v}{R\sqrt{32gRS_0}} + \frac{k_s}{14{\cdot}8R}\right)$$

$$= -\sqrt{32 \times 9{\cdot}806}\,[\log(39{\cdot}256 + 126{\cdot}943) - 6{\cdot}0] = 66{\cdot}95$$

From Eq. (3.3)

$$U = C\sqrt{RS_0} = 66{\cdot}95\sqrt{0{\cdot}7984 \times 0{\cdot}001} = 1{\cdot}892\,\text{m/s}$$

$$Q = AU = 7{\cdot}922 \times 1{\cdot}892 = 14{\cdot}99\,\text{m}^3/\text{s}$$

This shows that the accuracy of the computed depth of flow is greater than 99·9%.

Example 5.12: A trapezoidal channel with the following data, is laid at a bed slope of 1:1000. If the discharge rate is $15\,m^3/s$, calculate the depth of flow.

$$B = 2\cdot0\,m$$
$$m_1 = m_2 = 1\cdot0$$
$$k_s = 1\cdot5\,mm$$
$$v = 12\cdot5 \times 10^{-6}\,m^2/s$$

Solution: Following the same procedure as used in the previous example, we obtain $y = 1\cdot8273\,m$. Again, we examine the accuracy of the solution by verifying the discharge rate.

$$y = 1\cdot8273\,m$$

$$P = 2\cdot0 + 5\cdot1684 = 7\cdot1684\,m$$

$$A = 1\cdot8273 \times 3\cdot8273 = 6\cdot9936\,m^2$$

$$R = A/P = 0\cdot9756\,m$$

$$\frac{k_s}{14\cdot8R} = \frac{0\cdot0015}{14\cdot8 \times 0\cdot9756} = 103\cdot884 \times 10^{-6}$$

$$\frac{1\cdot255v}{R\sqrt{32gRS_0}} = \frac{1\cdot255 \times 12\cdot5 \times 10^{-6}}{0\cdot9756\sqrt{32 \times 9\cdot806 \times 0\cdot9756 \times 0\cdot001}}$$

$$= 29\cdot062 \times 10^{-6}$$

From Eq. (5.27)

$$C = -\sqrt{32g}\log\left(\frac{1\cdot255v}{R\sqrt{32gRS_0}} + \frac{k_s}{14\cdot8R}\right)$$

$$= -\sqrt{32 \times 9\cdot806}[\log(29\cdot062 + 103\cdot884) - 6\cdot0] = 68\cdot666$$

From Eq. (3.3)

$$U = C\sqrt{RS_0} = 68\cdot666\sqrt{0\cdot9756 \times 0\cdot001} = 2\cdot145\,m/s$$

$$Q = AU = 6\cdot9936 \times 2\cdot145 = 15\cdot0\,m^3/s$$

References

[5.1] BLASIUS H., *Das Ahnlichkeitsgesetz bei Reibugsvorgangen in Flussigkeiten*, Forsch Arb., Ing-Wes. No. 131, Berlin, 1913.

[5.2] STANTON T.E. and PANNAL J.R., 'Similarity of Motion in Relation to Surface Friction of Fluids', Phil. Trans. Roy. Soc., **214A**, 1914, 199–224.

[5.3] SCHLICHTING H., *Boundary Layer Theory*, translated from German by J. Kestin, McGraw-Hill, New York, 1968, ch. XX.

[5.4] COLEBROOK C.F., 'Turbulent Flow in Pipes with Particular Reference to the Transition Region between the Smooth and Rough Pipe Laws', J. Inst. Civ. Engrs, **11**, 1939, 133–156.

[5.5] WILLIAMSON J., *The Law of Flow in Rough Pipes*, La Houille Blanche, 1951, Vol. 6, No. 5, 738–757.

[5.6] MOODY L.F., 'Friction Factors for Pipe Flow', Trans ASME, **66**, 1944, 671.

[5.7] Department of the Environment, *Charts for the Hydraulic Design of Channels and Pipes*, HMSO, 4th edn, 1978.

[5.8] WALLINGFORD H.R. and BARR D.I.H., *Tables for Hydraulic Design of Pipes, Sewers and Channels*, Thomas Telford, London, 1998.

[5.9] STREETER V.L., *Fluid Mechanics*, McGraw-Hill, 1981.

6

Critical flow in channels

Critical flow results when the inertial force equals the gravity force acting in the direction of flow. The depth of flow, when it is critical, is intrinsically important in the computation of varied flow, for it is the only cross section at which the depth can be determined from the rate of discharge and, therefore, can be treated as a control section. The main contents of this chapter pertain to the determination of critical depth for channels of conventional shapes. Also included in the chapter are a brief description of the e–y curve, and the equation of the hydraulic jump.

6.1 Minimum specific energy, critical flow

The basis of the computation of varied flow in channels is the concept of specific energy and, more importantly, its variation with the depth of flow. Let us begin by recalling Eq. (2.43), and set the differential coefficient of e to zero. The result is

$$\frac{de}{dy} = 1 - \frac{Q^2}{gA^3}\frac{dA}{dy} = 0$$

To simplify the argument, replace dA/dy by T, the top width, which reduces the equation to

$$\frac{Q^2 T}{gA^3} = 1 \tag{6.1}$$

This equation establishes the existence of a cross section which, if its dimensions satisfy Eq. (6.1), contains minimum specific energy.

Next, by substituting U^2 for Q^2/A^2, and D for A/T, and taking the square root, we obtain

$$U = \sqrt{gD} \tag{6.2}$$

From this equation we infer that, at minimum specific energy, the velocity of flow is equal to the velocity (celerity) of small-height gravity waves in shallow waters (see reference [6.1]). Since a gravity wave can only travel downstream when $U > \sqrt{gD}$, and upstream when $U < \sqrt{gD}$, Eq. (6.2) is the condition of *critical flow*. This approach leads to the classification of flow into *sub-critical* when $U < \sqrt{gD}$, and *super-critical* when $U > \sqrt{gD}$. The cross section of flow at which the specific energy is minimum is called the *critical cross section* or, simply *critical section*. It can be verified that, at critical cross section, the inertial force equals the gravity force, which is indicated by the Froude number having the value 1·0 (see Eq. (2.46)).

The criterion for the flow to be critical can also be derived by minimizing the specific force, described in section 2.10. This is as follows:

Recalling Eq. (2.34)

$$\Sigma = \frac{Q^2}{gA} + A\bar{y} \tag{2.34}$$

and substituting in it the following expression for $\bar{y}$

$$\bar{y} = \frac{1}{A} \int y dA$$

that is,

$$A\bar{y} = \int y dA = \int y \frac{dA}{dy} dy = \int y T dy$$

we obtain

$$\Sigma = \frac{Q^2}{gA} + \int y T dy$$

which, on differentiating with respect to y, gives

$$\frac{d\Sigma}{dy} = -\frac{Q^2}{gA^2} \frac{dA}{dy} + \int T dy$$

that is,

$$\frac{d\Sigma}{dy} = -\frac{Q^2 T}{gA^2} + A$$

Replacing Q/A by U, this reduces to

$$\frac{d\Sigma}{dy} = -\frac{U^2 T}{g} + A$$

Setting $d\Sigma/dy$ to zero, we obtain

$$\frac{U^2}{g} = \frac{A}{T} = D$$

which is the same as Eq. (6.2).

6.2 Critical depth

The depth of the critical section is called the *critical depth* y_c, and it occurs regularly in the computation of varied flow. In recognition of the existence of the critical section, all hydraulic properties associated with it are denoted by adding the suffix c to their symbols, for example, the symbol D_c denotes the hydraulic depth of the critical section. An important aspect of Eq. (6.1) is that it is a relationship only between the geometry of the cross section of flow and the rate of discharge, and is independent of the channel gradient.

Introducing the critical values into Eq. (2.42)

$$e = y + \frac{U^2}{2g} \tag{2.42}$$

we find that the minimum specific energy e_{min} is given by

$$e_{min} = y_c + \frac{U_c^2}{2g} \tag{6.3}$$

and, from Eq. (6.2), the critical velocity U_c satisfies the equation

$$U_c^2 = gD_c \tag{6.4}$$

By eliminating U_c^2 between the last two equations, we obtain expression for the minimum specific energy in terms of the critical depth and the corresponding hydraulic depth:

$$e_{min} = y_c + \frac{1}{2}D_c \tag{6.5}$$

For a rectangular channel, since $D_c = y_c$,

$$e_{min} = \frac{3}{2}y_c \tag{6.6}$$

6.3 Determination of critical depth

The critical depth y_c is determined by solving Eq. (6.1) which is written as

$$F = gA_c^3 - Q^2 T_c = 0 \tag{6.7}$$

in which A_c and T_c are replaced by their expressions in terms of y_c. If the resulting equation is solvable by elementary means, then this leads to the exact determination of the critical depth. For instance, critical depths for rectangular, triangular or parabolic channels can be determined exactly. Channels of other shapes, which include trapezoidal and circular, Eq. (6.7) can only be solved numerically. Let us begin with the exact determination of the critical depth.

6.4 Exact determination of the critical depth

The exact determination of the critical depth is restricted to the following geometrical shapes:

(a) Rectangular
(b) Triangular
(c) Parabolic

6.4.1 Rectangular channel

For a rectangular channel, we have

$$A_c = By_c$$
$$T_c = B$$

Substitution of these expressions in Eq. (6.7) gives

$$y_c = \left(\frac{Q^2}{gB^2}\right)^{1/3} \tag{6.8}$$

This equation is sometimes written as

$$y_c = \left(\frac{q^2}{g} \right)^{1/3} \tag{6.9}$$

where q is the rate of discharge per unit width of the channel.

It can be verified that when the rate of flow in a channel of length L varies linearly, as is the case of a linear drainage channel, the critical depth y_c at a distance x from the upstream end is related to the critical depth $y_{c,L}$ if it were to occur at the outlet ($x = L$), by the equation

$$y_c = \left(\frac{x}{L} \right)^{2/3} y_{c,L} \tag{6.10}$$

this relationship will be used in locating the control section (see Chapter 8).

6.4.2 Triangular channel

For a triangular channel, we have

$$A_c = \frac{1}{2}(m_1 + m_2)y_c^2$$

$$T_c = (m_1 + m_2)y_c$$

Substitution of these expressions in Eq. (6.7) leads to the determination of y_c.

$$y_c^5 = \frac{8Q^2}{g(m_1 + m_2)^2}$$

that is,

$$y_c = \left(\frac{2Q^2}{gm^2} \right)^{1/5} \tag{6.11}$$

where

$$m = \frac{m_1 + m_2}{2} \tag{6.12}$$

6.4.3 Parabolic channel

For a parabolic channel, we have from Eq. (2.10)

$$A_c = \frac{2}{3} T_c y_c$$

where T_c and y_c are related to the overall dimensions, T and y, of the cross section by the equation

$$T_c^2 = \frac{T^2}{y} y_c$$

When these are substituted in Eq. (6.7), the result is

$$y_c = \left(\frac{27}{8} \frac{Q^2 y}{g T^2} \right)^{1/4} \tag{6.13}$$

6.5 Numerical determination of critical depth

Among the geometrical shapes commonly used in drainage channels, but for which critical depths cannot be obtained exactly, are trapezoidal and circular. In the following section the application of the Newton-Raphson method, discussed in Appendix A, for the numerical determination of the critical depths for such shapes is demonstrated.

6.5.1 Critical depth of a trapezoidal channel

For a trapezoidal channel (Fig. 6.1), transform Eq. (6.7) in terms of y_c by making use of the following expressions:

$$A_c = (B + m y_c) y_c \tag{6.14}$$

$$T_c = B + 2 m y_c \tag{6.15}$$

From the last equation

$$\frac{dT_c}{dy_c} = 2m \tag{6.16}$$

where

$$m = \frac{1}{2}(m_1 + m_2)$$

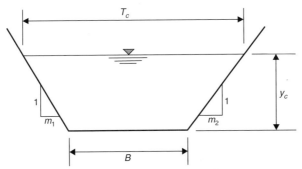

Figure 6.1 *Critical dimensions of a trapezoidal channel.*

In solving Eq. (6.7) by the Newton-Raphson method, we use the expression for the critical depth in a rectangular channel, that is

$$y_{c0} = \left(\frac{Q^2}{gB^2} \right)^{1/3}$$

as the initial trial value of y_c

Example 6.1: Find the critical depth of flow in a trapezoidal channel with the following data (see Fig. 6.1):

$$B = 2 \cdot 0 \text{ m} \qquad m_1 = 1 \cdot 0 \qquad m_2 = 2 \cdot 0 \qquad Q = 2 \cdot 0 \text{ m}^3/\text{s}$$

Solution:

$$m = \frac{1}{2}(m_1 + m_2) = 1 \cdot 5$$

$$y_{c0} = \left(\frac{Q^2}{gB^2} \right)^{1/3} = \left(\frac{2}{9 \cdot 806 \times 4} \right)^{1/3} = 0 \cdot 4672 \text{ m}$$

Iteration 1

$$T_{c0} = B + 2my_{c0} = 2 \cdot 0 + 3 \cdot 0 \times 0 \cdot 4672 = 3 \cdot 4016 \text{ m}$$

$$A_{c0} = \frac{1}{2}(B + T_{c0})y_{c0} = \frac{1}{2}(5 \cdot 4016)(0 \cdot 4672) = 1 \cdot 2618 \text{ m}^2$$

From Eq. (6.7)

$$F(y_{c0}) = gT_{c0}^3 - Q^2T_{c0}$$
$$= 9{\cdot}806(1{\cdot}2618)^3 - 4{\cdot}0 \times 3{\cdot}4016 = 6{\cdot}0935$$

$$F'(y_{c0}) = 3gA_{c0}^2T_{c0} - 2Q^2\,m$$
$$= 3 \times 9{\cdot}806(1{\cdot}2618)^2 \times 3{\cdot}4016 - 4{\cdot}0 \times 3{\cdot}0 = 147{\cdot}3226$$

$$\delta y_{c0} = -\frac{F(y_{c0})}{F'(y_{c0})} = -\frac{6{\cdot}0935}{147{\cdot}3226} = -0{\cdot}0414 \text{ m}$$

Iteration 2

$$y_{c1} = y_{c0} + \delta y_{c0} = 0{\cdot}4672 - 0{\cdot}0414 = 0{\cdot}4258 \text{ m}$$
$$T_{c1} = B + 2my_{c1} = 2{\cdot}0 + 3{\cdot}0 \times 0{\cdot}4258 = 3{\cdot}2774 \text{ m}$$
$$A_{c1} = \frac{1}{2}(B + T_{c1})y_{c1} = \frac{1}{2}(5{\cdot}2774)(0{\cdot}4258) = 1{\cdot}1236$$
$$F(y_{c1}) = 9{\cdot}806(1{\cdot}1236)^3 - 4{\cdot}0 \times 3{\cdot}2774 = 0{\cdot}8004$$
$$F'(y_{c1}) = 3 \times 9{\cdot}806(1{\cdot}1236)^2 \times 3{\cdot}2774 - 4{\cdot}0 \times 3{\cdot}0 = 109{\cdot}7212$$
$$\delta y_{c1} = -\frac{F(y_{c1})}{F'(y_{c1})} = -\frac{0{\cdot}8004}{109{\cdot}7212} = -0{\cdot}0073 \text{ m}$$

Iteration 3

$$y_{c2} = y_{c1} + \delta y_{c2} = 0{\cdot}4258 - 0{\cdot}0073 = 0{\cdot}4185 \text{ m}$$
$$T_{c2} = B + 2my_{c2} = 2{\cdot}0 + 3{\cdot}0 \times 0{\cdot}4185 = 3{\cdot}2555 \text{ m}$$
$$A_{c2} = (B + T_{c2})y_{c2} = \frac{1}{2}(5{\cdot}2555)(0{\cdot}4185) = 1{\cdot}0997 \text{ m}^2$$
$$F(y_{c2}) = 9{\cdot}806(1{\cdot}0997)^3 - 4{\cdot}0 \times 3{\cdot}2555 = 0{\cdot}01911$$
$$F'(y_{c2}) = 3 \times 9{\cdot}806(1{\cdot}0997)^2 \times 3{\cdot}2555 - 4{\cdot}0 \times 3{\cdot}0 = 103{\cdot}8189$$
$$\delta y_{c2} = -\frac{F(y_{c2})}{F'(y_{c2})} = -\frac{0{\cdot}01911}{103{\cdot}8189} = -0{\cdot}0002 \text{ m}$$
$$y_{c3} = y_{c2} + \delta y_{c2} = 0{\cdot}4185 - 0{\cdot}0002 = 0{\cdot}4183 \text{ m}$$

$$T_{c3} = 2 \cdot 0 + 3 \cdot 0 \times 0 \cdot 4183 = 3 \cdot 2549 \text{ m}$$

$$A_{c3} = \frac{1}{2}(2 \cdot 0 + 3 \cdot 2549)(0 \cdot 4183) = 1 \cdot 0991 \text{ m}^2$$

$$F(y_{c3}) = 9 \cdot 806(1 \cdot 0991)^3 - 4 \cdot 0 \times 3 \cdot 2549 = 0 \cdot 0002$$

Since $F(y_{c3})$ is sufficiently close to 0, we accept $y_c = y_{c3} = 0 \cdot 4183$ m.

6.5.2 Critical depth in a circular pipe

For a circular pipe (Fig. 6.2), we have

$$A_c = \frac{1}{4}(\theta_c - \sin\theta_c \cos\theta_c)d^2 \tag{6.17}$$

$$T_c = d \sin\theta_c \tag{6.18}$$

$$\frac{dT_c}{dy_c} = \frac{dT_c}{d\theta_c}\frac{d\theta_c}{dy_c} = 2\cot\theta_c \tag{6.19}$$

When the expressions for A_c and T_c are substituted in Eq. (6.7), the result is

$$(\theta_c - \sin\theta_c \cos\theta_c)^3 = \frac{64Q^3}{gd^5}\sin\theta_c \tag{6.20}$$

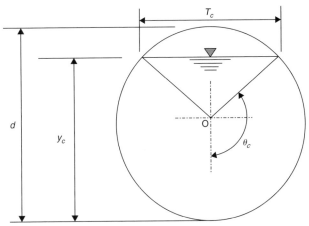

Figure 6.2 *Critical dimensions of a circular pipe.*

As an initial trial value of y_c is taken as

$$y_{c0} = 1\cdot033\left(\frac{Q}{d\sqrt{g}}\right)^{2/3} + 0\cdot083d \tag{6.21}$$

This value is found accurate within the interval $0\cdot3 < y_c/d < 0\cdot9$, that is, $66° < \theta_c = 143°$.

The corresponding value of θ is obtained from the equation

$$\cos\theta_c = 1 - 2\frac{y_c}{d} \tag{6.22}$$

Example 6.2: Find the critical depth of flow in a $0\cdot3$ m diameter circular pipe carrying a discharge of 40 l/s.

Solution: From Eq. (6.21)

$$y_{c0} = 1\cdot033\left(\frac{0\cdot04}{0\cdot3\sqrt{9\cdot806}}\right)^{2/3} + 0\cdot083(0\cdot3) = 0\cdot1509 \text{ m}$$

Iteration 1

$$\theta_{c0} = \cos^{-1}\left(1 - 2\frac{y_{c0}}{d}\right) = 90\cdot343° = 1\cdot5765^R$$

$$\sin\theta_{c0} = 1\cdot0$$

$$\cos\theta_{c0} = -0\cdot006$$

$$A_{c0} = \frac{1}{4}(1\cdot5765 + 0\cdot006)(0\cdot09) = 0\cdot0356 \text{ m}^2$$

$$T_{c0} = 0\cdot3 \text{ m}$$

From Eq. (6.7)

$$F(y_{c0}) = gA_{c0}^3 - Q^2T_{c0} = 9\cdot806(0\cdot0356)^3 - 0\cdot0016 \times 0.3$$

$$= -0\cdot000038$$

$$\frac{dT_{c0}}{dy_c} = -2\cot\theta_{c0} = -0\cdot012$$

$$F'(y_{c0}) = 3gA_{c0}^2 T_{c0} - Q^2 \frac{dT_c}{dy}$$

$$= 3 \times 9{\cdot}806(0{\cdot}0356)^2 \times 0{\cdot}3 + 0{\cdot}0016 \times 0{\cdot}012 = 0{\cdot}0112$$

$$\delta y_{c0} = \frac{0{\cdot}000038}{0{\cdot}0112} = 0{\cdot}0034 \text{ m}$$

$$y_{c1} = 0{\cdot}1509 + 0{\cdot}0034 = 0{\cdot}1543 \text{ m}$$

$$\theta_{c1} = \cos^{-1}\left(1 - 2\frac{y_{c1}}{d}\right) = \cos^{-1}\left(1 - 2\frac{0{\cdot}1543}{3}\right) = 91{\cdot}64° = 1{\cdot}5995^R$$

$$A_{c1} = \frac{1}{4}(1{\cdot}5995 + 0{\cdot}0287) \times 0{\cdot}09 = 0{\cdot}0366 \text{ m}^2$$

$$T_{c1} = 0{\cdot}3 \times 0{\cdot}9996 = 0{\cdot}2999 \text{ m}$$

$$F(y_{c1}) = gA_{c1}^3 - Q^2 T_{c1} = 9{\cdot}806(0{\cdot}0356)^3 - 0{\cdot}0016 \times 0{\cdot}2999 = 0$$

This establishes the accuracy of the value $y_c = 0{\cdot}1543$ m.

6.5.3   Critical depth of a compound (U-shaped) section

The cross section of a U-shaped drainage channel shown in Fig. 6.3 is made up of a rectangle and a semicircle. If the water level is below level 1, that is, within the semicircular invert, then the critical depth is determined in accordance with the method described in section 6.5.2. If the water level is higher than the semicircular part, then

$$A_c = B(y_c - a) + \frac{1}{2}\pi a^2 \tag{6.23}$$

$$T_c = B \tag{6.24}$$

Hence, from Eq. (6.1)

$$\left[B(y_c - a) + \frac{1}{2}\pi a^2\right]^3 = \frac{Q^2 B}{g}$$

that is,

$$y_c = \left(\frac{Q^2}{gB^2}\right)^{1/3} - \frac{1}{2}\frac{\pi a^2}{B} + a$$

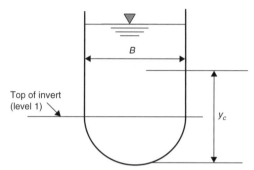

Figure 6.3 *Critical dimensions of a U-shaped channel.*

Since $a = B/2$, we have

$$y_c = \left(\frac{Q^2}{gB^2}\right)^{1/3} + \frac{4-\pi}{8}B \tag{6.25}$$

Example 6.3: Find the critical depth of flow in a 0·4 m wide compound section (Fig. 6.3) with maximum discharge rate at the outlet = 200 l/s.

Solution:

If the critical depth is just up to the top of the semicircular portion, then

$$A_c = 0·02\,\pi \qquad D_c = 0·05\,\pi$$

From Eq. (6.2)

$$U_c = \sqrt{9·806 \times 0·05\,\pi} = 1·2411 \text{ m/s}$$

$$Q_{max} = 1000(0·02\,\pi)(1·2411) = 77·98 \text{ l/s} \,(<200 \text{ l/s})$$

Hence, the water surface is above level 1.
From Eq. (6.25)

$$y_c = \left(\frac{0·04}{9·806 \times 0·16}\right)^{1/3} + \frac{0·4(4-\pi)}{8} = 0·294 + 0·043 = 0·337 \text{ m}$$

Check for discharge:

$$A_c = 0·02\,\pi + 0·4(0·337 - 0·2) = 0·1176 \text{ m}^2$$

$$D_c = 0·1176/0·4 = 0·294 \text{ m}$$

From Eq. (6.2)

$$U_c = \sqrt{9\cdot806 \times 0\cdot294} = 1\cdot698 \text{ m/s}$$

Therefore,

$$Q_c = 1\cdot698 \times 0\cdot1176 = 0\cdot2 \text{ m}^3/\text{s}$$

6.6 The specific energy equation

The understanding of flow with varying specific energy can be advanced further by applying Eq. (2.43) to a cross section of which the hydraulic properties can be determined readily. For this purpose, let us consider a rectangular channel that fulfils this requirement and, due to its extreme simplicity, is widely used, both in the analytical treatment and practical application of varied flow. For a given rate of discharge q per unit width, Eq. (2.43) is written as

$$e = y + \frac{q^2}{2gy^2} \tag{6.26}$$

that is,

$$y^3 - ey^2 + \frac{q^2}{2g} = 0 \tag{6.27}$$

This equation, being a cubic in y, has three real roots, say, y_1, y_2 and y_3, which satisfy the following equations:

$$y_1 + y_2 + y_3 = e$$

$$y_1 y_2 + y_2 y_3 + y_3 y_1 = 0$$

$$y_1 y_2 y_3 = -\frac{q^2}{2g}$$

From the first and third of these equations, we infer that only one of the roots of Eq. (6.27), say, y_3 is negative, which must be ignored, while both of the remaining roots y_1 and y_2 are positive. An interpretation of this is that, for a given single value of specific energy, there are two possible depths of flow, known as the *conjugate depths*. The existence of the conjugate depths introduces the possibility of changeover from one depth of flow to another, over a short distance. This, almost sudden, change of depth is referred to as a *local phenomenon*, which may occur either as the *hydraulic jump* or as a *hydraulic drop*. In a hydraulic jump the depth changes from a lower value to a higher value, while opposite is the case of a hydraulic drop. Any of these changes in the depth may be caused by, say, a sudden change in the bed slope or the cross section of the channel.

6.7 The specific energy curve

The specific energy curve, which we will call the *e–y* curve, is the graph of Eq. (6.27) for a given value of q. One such graph, which corresponds to an arbitrary value of q, is shown in Fig. 6.4. Assuming that this curve represents, qualitatively, a typical *e–y* curve, the following properties of flow can be deduced from it:

(*a*) In the region $y < y_c$, the specific energy increases as y decreases. This is evident from the differential coefficient of e with respect to y, that is,

$$\frac{de}{dy} = 1 - \frac{q^2}{gy^3} = 1 - \left(\frac{y_c}{y}\right)^3 \tag{6.28}$$

which is negative for $y < y_c$. It has to be so. For, in order to maintain the discharge rate q, the velocity in this region has to increase, and remain above critical. Consequently, the flow in the region is super-critical.

From Eq. (6.28), it follows that the specific energy tends to infinity as y tends to zero. This means that the e axis is an asymptote of the *e–y* curve.

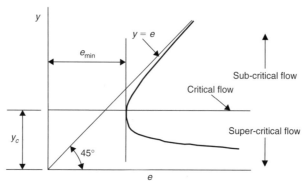

Figure 6.4 *A typical e–y curve.*

(b) At $y = y_c$, the specific energy is minimum, its value given by Eq. (6.6). The flow at this depth is critical.

(c) In the region $y > y_c$, the specific energy increases with y, while the difference between e and y tends to zero as y increases to infinity. This means that, the straight line $y = e$ is the second asymptote of the e–y curve.

(d) In contrast with (a), a rising depth of flow causes lowering of the velocity which, therefore, stays below the critical velocity. Hence, the flow in this region is sub-critical.

(e) For all values of e other than e_{min} one of the two conjugate depths corresponds to sub-critical, and the other to super-critical flow.

6.8 Hydraulic jump and hydraulic drop

Whenever there is a sudden change in the bed slope or the cross section of a channel, the pattern of flow changes. For instance, a sudden widening of the channel will cause the water to lose its energy content and, as a result, the depth of flow will rise, see Example 6.4. It can be found from the e–y curve that, in such a situation, the flow will change from super-critical to sub-critical. A hydraulic jump cannot form when the flow is already sub-critical.

A hydraulic jump is mostly applied when the energy of flow needs to be dissipated, an example of which is the water flowing over spillways. Another application of hydraulic jump is in raising or maintaining the water level for irrigation purposes. For a detailed account of hydraulic jump, see references [6.1, 6.2, 6.3].

A *free outfall*, which is a regular feature of a drainage channel, is a special case of hydraulic drop in which the bottom of the channel is totally discontinued, and the water surface upstream of the outfall adjusts itself to allow the water to seek the point of lowest energy. This point coincides with the outfall. However, the specific energy at the outfall may, or may not, be minimum in the mathematical sense, that is, the tangent to the flow profile may, or may not, be parallel to the channel bed.

6.8.1 Hydraulic jump equation

The derivation of the equation of hydraulic jump follows the momentum equation relating the specific forces at the two cross sections, one immediately before, and the other after the jump (see Fig. 6.5). Considering a rectangular channel, substitute into Eq. (2.33)

$$\frac{Q^2}{gA_1} + A_1\bar{y}_1 = \frac{Q^2}{gA_2} + A_2\bar{y}_2 \tag{2.33}$$

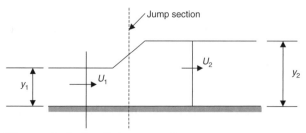

Figure 6.5 *Diagram for hydraulic jump equation.*

the following properties

$$Q = U_1 A_1 = U_2 A_2$$

$$A_1 = B y_1 \qquad \bar{y}_1 = \frac{y_1}{2}$$

$$A_2 = B y_2 \qquad \bar{y}_2 = \frac{y_2}{2}$$

This results in

$$\frac{U_1^2 y_1}{g} + \frac{1}{2} y_1^2 = \frac{U_2^2 y_2}{g} + \frac{1}{2} y_2^2 \tag{6.29}$$

Since,

$$\frac{U_1^2}{g y_1} = F_1^2$$

and

$$\frac{U_2^2}{g y_2} = \frac{U_1^2 y_1^2}{g y_2^3} = \frac{F_1^2 y_1^3}{y_2^3}$$

we have from Eq. (6.29)

$$F_1^2 y_1^2 + \frac{1}{2} y_1^2 = F_1^2 \frac{y_1^3}{y_2} + \frac{1}{2} y_2^2$$

that is,

$$\left(\frac{y_2}{y_1} \right)^3 - \left(2F_1^2 + 1 \right) \frac{y_2}{y_1} + 2F_1^2 = 0$$

Ignoring the trivial root $y_2 = y_1$, and the negative root, we obtain the hydraulic jump equation

$$\frac{y_2}{y_1} = \frac{1}{2}\left(\sqrt{8F_1^2 + 1} - 1\right) \tag{6.30}$$

which gives

$$F_1^2 = \frac{1}{2}\frac{y_2}{y_1}\left(\frac{y_2}{y_1} + 1\right) \tag{6.31}$$

Similarly, we obtain

$$\frac{y_1}{y_2} = \frac{1}{2}\left(\sqrt{8F_2^2 + 1} - 1\right) \tag{6.32}$$

and

$$F_2^2 = \frac{1}{2}\frac{y_1}{y_2}\left(\frac{y_1}{y_2} + 1\right) \tag{6.33}$$

6.8.2 Head loss in hydraulic jump

From the continuity equation

$$U_1 y_1 = U_2 y_2$$

we obtain

$$F_1^2 y_1^3 = F_2^2 y_2^3 \tag{6.34}$$

The combination of this equation with the energy equation,

$$\frac{U_1^2}{2g} + y_1 = \frac{U_2^2}{2g} + y_2 + h_j \tag{6.35}$$

where h_j is the head loss due to the hydraulic jump, gives

$$\frac{1}{2}F_1^2 y_1 + y_1 = \frac{1}{2}F_2^2 y_2 + y_2 + h_j \tag{6.36}$$

The elimination of F_1 and F_2 between Eqs (6.31), (6.33) and (6.36) gives

$$h_j = \frac{(y_2 - y_1)^3}{4y_1 y_2} \qquad (6.37)$$

Example 6.4: A hydraulic jump occurs in a 1·2 m wide rectangular channel. If the velocity and the depth of flow before the jump are 7 m/s and 0·8 m, determine (*a*) the Froude number after the jump, (*b*) the velocity and depth after the jump, and (*c*) head loss due to the jump.

Solution: $U_1 = 7·0$ m/s $\quad y_1 = 0·8$ m

(*a*) From Eq. (6.30)

$$y_2 = \frac{1}{2}\left(\sqrt{8 \times 6·246 + 1} - 1\right) \times 0·8 = 2.456 \text{ m}$$

From Eq. (6.34)

$$F_2^2 = F_1^2 \left(\frac{y_1}{y_2}\right)^3 = 6·246 \left(\frac{0·8}{2·456}\right)^3 = 0·216$$

Therefore,

$$F_2 = 0·465$$

(*b*) $y_2 = 2·456$ m

$$U_2 = \frac{y_1}{y_2} U_1 = \frac{0·8}{2·456} \times 7·0 = 2·28 \text{ m/s}$$

(*c*) From Eq. (6.37)

$$h_j = \frac{(2·456 - 0·8)^3}{4 \times 0·8 \times 2·456} = 0·578 \text{ m}$$

6.9 Critical slope

Typically, a uniform flow is sub-critical. However, by varying the slope, the flow in a channel can be changed to super-critical, so that the depth of flow becomes critical and, to satisfy the condition of uniformity of flow, remains critical in the entire channel. This slope is called the *critical slope* S_c. The slope of a channel, if less than the critical slope, is classified as *mild*, and *steep* if greater. For a detailed discussion on the effect of slope on flow profiles, see section 9.3 of reference [6.2]. The determination of the critical slope is illustrated by the following example:

Example 6.5: Find the critical slope of a 150 mm wide rectangular channel with discharge capacity of 22·22 l/s (Manning's $n = 0·015$).

Solution:

From Eq. (6.8)

$$y_c = \left[\frac{1}{9·806} \left(\frac{0·02222}{0·15} \right)^2 \right]^{1/3} = 0·1308 \text{ m}$$

$$A_c = 0·15 \times 0·1308 = 0·0196 \text{ m}^2$$

$$P_c = 0·15 + 0·2616 = 0·4116 \text{ m}$$

$$R_c = \frac{A_c}{P_c} = \frac{0·0196}{0·4116} = 0·0476 \text{ m}$$

$$U_c = \frac{Q_{max}}{A_c} = \frac{0·02222}{0·0196} = 1·134 \text{ m/s}$$

From Eq. (3.5)

$$U_c = \frac{1}{n} R_c^{2/3} S_c^{1/2}$$

that is,

$$1·134 = \frac{1}{0·015} (0·0476)^{2/3} S_c^{1/2} = 8·755 \sqrt{S_c}$$

Therefore,

$$S_c = \left(\frac{1·134}{8·755} \right)^2 = 0·0168$$

References

[6.1] BAKHMETEFF B.A., *Hydraulics of Open Channels*, Part III, McGraw-Hill, New York, 1932, p. 227.

[6.2] WOODWARD S.M., *Hydraulics of Steady Flow in Open Channels*, John Wiley, New York, 1941, chs III, IV.

[6.3] STREETER V.L. and WYLIE E.B., *Fluid Mechanics*, McGraw-Hill, Singapore, 1981, p. 135.

7

Computation of varied flow I: flow profiles

Derived in Chapter 3, the differential equation of gradually varied flow is solvable exactly only for horizontal channels of simple geometry, and in the hypothetical situation of flow without loss. In this chapter, consideration is given to the solution of the equation under these restrictions to determine if the solution has any meaning. Later, the chapter considers the numerical solution, in the light of the step method, and outlines the procedure for obtaining flow profiles for channels of various elementary shapes. The method generally adopted is the well-known Newton-Raphson method. The chapter also contains the flow profiles for some arbitrarily shaped channels. For a U-shaped channel the flow profile is calculated using the Runge-Kutta method.

7.1 Smooth channel laid at zero gradient

Consider a channel of an arbitrary shape, laid at zero gradient and having no friction. Under these conditions, Eq. (3.15):

$$\frac{dy}{dx} = \frac{S_0 - S_f - (2Q/gA^2)(dQ/dx)}{1 - (Q^2/gA^2D)} \tag{3.15}$$

reduces to

$$\frac{dy}{dx} = \frac{(2Q/gA^2)(dQ/dx)}{(Q^2/gA^2D) - 1} \tag{7.1}$$

In a linear drainage channel, carrying a maximum discharge Q_{max} at the outlet, the rate of flow at a distance x from the upstream end is given by

$$Q = Q_{max}\frac{x}{L} \tag{7.2}$$

where L is the length of the channel.

With the elimination of Q in Eqs (7.1) and (7.2)

$$2x\frac{dx}{dy} - \frac{1}{D}x^2 = -\frac{gA^2L^2}{Q_{max}^2} \tag{7.3}$$

which is a linear differential equation in x^2, and has the integrating factor

$$\psi = \exp\left(\int-\frac{dy}{D}\right) = \exp\left(\int-\frac{Tdy}{A}\right)$$

$$= \exp\left(\int-\frac{dA}{A}\right) = \exp\left[ln\left(\frac{1}{A}\right)\right] = \frac{1}{A}$$

Hence, the solution of Eq. (7.3) is

$$\frac{x^2}{A} = -\int\frac{gAL^2}{Q_{max}^2}dy + c$$

that is,

$$x^2 = -\frac{gAL^2}{Q_{max}^2}I + cA \tag{7.4}$$

where

$$I = \int A\,dy \tag{7.5}$$

and c is the constant of integration.

While the integral can be evaluated from the geometry of the cross section, the constant of integration can be determined only if the depth of flow is known at some cross section of the channel. For instance, if there is a free outfall at the downstream end, then the depth of flow there will be critical, and will be obtainable from the known rate of discharge at the outlet. Hence, by setting $x = 0$ at the upstream end of the channel, and imposing on Eq. (7.4) the condition

$$(y)_{x=L} = y_c$$

we obtain

$$c = \frac{L^2}{A_c} + \frac{gL^2}{Q_{max}^2} I_c \tag{7.6}$$

where A_c is the cross-sectional area of flow at the critical section (outlet in this case), and I_c is the value of the integral defined by Eq. (7.5) at $x = L$. Hence, the complete solution of Eq. (7.3) is

$$\frac{x^2}{L^2} = \frac{A}{A_c} + \frac{gA}{Q_{max}^2}(I_c - I) \tag{7.7}$$

7.1.1 Rectangular channel

For a rectangular channel, defined by its width B, and the depth of flow y, we have

$$A = By \qquad I = \frac{1}{2}By^2$$

$$A_c = By_c \qquad I_c = \frac{1}{2}By_c^2$$

Substitution of these expressions in Eq. (7.7) results in

$$\frac{x^2}{L^2} = \frac{y}{y_c} + \frac{gyB^2}{2Q_{max}^2}(y_c^2 - y^2)$$

Since

$$y_c = \left(\frac{Q_{max}^2}{B^2 g}\right)^{1/3} \tag{6.8}$$

the above equation reduces to

$$\left(\frac{x}{L}\right)^2 = \frac{y}{y_c} + \frac{1}{2}\frac{y}{y_c^3}(y_c^2 - y^2)$$

that is,

$$\left(\frac{x}{L}\right)^2 = \frac{3}{2}\left(\frac{y}{y_c}\right) - \frac{1}{2}\left(\frac{y}{y_c}\right)^3 \tag{7.8}$$

At the upstream end, we obtain from Eq. (7.8)

$$y = y_c \sqrt{3} \tag{7.9}$$

7.1.2 Triangular channel

For a triangular channel, defined by the side slopes m_1 and m_2, and the depth of flow y, we have

$$A = my^2 \qquad I = \frac{1}{3}my^3$$

$$A_c = my_c^2 \qquad I_c = \frac{1}{3}my_c^3$$

where

$$m = \frac{1}{2}(m_1 + m_2)$$

Substitution of these expressions in Eq. (7.7) results in

$$\frac{x^2}{L^2} = \frac{y^2}{y_c^2} + \frac{gm^2y^2}{3Q_{max}^2}(y_c^3 - y^3)$$

Since

$$y_c = \left(\frac{2Q_{max}^2}{gm^2}\right)^{1/5} \qquad \text{(see Eq. (6.11))}$$

the above equation reduces to

$$\left(\frac{x}{L}\right)^2 = \frac{y^2}{y_c^2} + \frac{2}{3}\frac{y^2}{y_c^5}(y_c^3 - y^3)$$

that is,

$$\left(\frac{x}{L}\right)^2 = \frac{5}{3}\left(\frac{y}{y_c}\right)^2 - \frac{2}{3}\left(\frac{y}{y_c}\right)^5 \tag{7.10}$$

At the upstream end, we obtain from Eq. (7.10)

$$y = y_c \sqrt[3]{2 \cdot 5} \tag{7.11}$$

Example 7.1: A horizontal rectangular channel, with closed top, is to carry discharge from a paved area 40 m wide. The intensity of rainfall on the area is 40 mm/h. If the width of the channel is 0·15 m, and the available depth 0·3 m, determine the maximum length of the channel. Ignore any loss due to friction, and assume that the runoff coefficient = 1·0.

Solution: From Eq. (1.1)

$$Q_{max} = \frac{(40)(40)}{36 \times 10^5} L = 0·4444 \times 10^{-3} L \text{ m}^3/\text{s}$$

For the channel to run full,

$$y = 0·3 \text{ m}$$

From Eq. (7.9)

$$y_c = 0·3/\sqrt{3} = 0·1732 \text{ m}$$

From Eq. (6.8)

$$\frac{Q_{max}^2}{gB^2} = y_c^3 = (0·1732)^3 = 0·005196$$

that is,

$$Q_{max} = 0·15\sqrt{(0·005196)(9·806)} = 0·03386 \text{ m}^3/\text{s}$$

Therefore,

$$L = \frac{0·03386 \times 10^4}{0·4444} = 76·2 \text{ m}$$

Example 7.2: The data for the design of a triangular channel, required to drain surplus rainwater from a road surface, are:

Effective width of carriageway	9·3 m	
Width of channel	0·9 m	
Side slopes	$m_1 = 1·0$	$m_2 = 5·0$
Duration of rainfall	11 min	
Storm return period	1 year	

The road is in a cutting (runoff coefficient 0·11). The average width of the cutting is 15·0 m. Ignoring the friction and the horizontal gradient, calculate the length of the channel.

Use the Bilham formula to determine the intensity of rainfall, and assume the road surface to be impervious of which the runoff coefficient is 1·0.

Solution:

From the Bilham formula

$$I = \frac{1}{D}\left[14\cdot14(ND)^{1/3\cdot55} - 2\cdot54\right] \tag{1.5}$$

we determine

$$I = \frac{60}{11}\left[14\cdot14\left(\frac{11}{60}\right)^{1/3\cdot55} - 2\cdot54\right] = 33\cdot97 \text{ mm/hr}$$

If W is the total width contributing to the channel flow, then

$$W = 9\cdot3 + 0\cdot9 + 0\cdot11 \times 15\cdot0 = 11\cdot85 \text{ m}$$

Let the channel length $= L$.
Taking $I = 35\cdot0$ mm/hr, we obtain from Eq. (1.1), above,

$$Q_{max} = \frac{C_r I A_s}{36 \times 10^5} = \frac{1\cdot0 \times 35\cdot0 \times 11\cdot85L}{3600} = 0\cdot1152L \text{ l/s}$$

Allowable depth of flow at the upstream end of the channel is given by

$$y_{max} = \frac{T}{m_1 + m_2} = \frac{0\cdot9}{6} = 0\cdot15 \text{ m}$$

From Eq. (7.11)

$$y_c = \frac{y_{max}}{\sqrt[3]{2\cdot5}} = \frac{0\cdot15}{\sqrt[3]{2\cdot5}} = 0\cdot1105 \text{ m}$$

From Eq. (6.11)

$$\frac{2Q_{max}^2}{gm^2} = y_c^5 = (0\cdot1105)^5 = 16\cdot49 \times 10^{-6}$$

that is,

$$Q_{max} = 3\cdot0\sqrt{\frac{(16\cdot49 \times 10^{-6})(9\cdot806)}{2}} = 0\cdot027 \text{ m}^3/\text{s}$$

Therefore,

$$L = \frac{0\cdot027 \times 10^3}{0\cdot1152} = 234 \text{ m}$$

7.2   The flow profile

A criterion for the adequacy of the design of a drainage channel is that, at no point, the depth of flow should exceed the available depth of the channel. For instance, the depth of flow in a roadside channel is governed by the width of flow or the height of the kerb and, in a combined kerb-drainage system, it is restricted by the internal height of the system. Hence, it becomes necessary to compute the depth of flow along the entire length of the channel. The plot of depth of flow against longitudinal distance, conventionally measured from the upstream end of a channel, is called the *flow profile*. An important application of the flow profile is found in determining the maximum length of a drainage system of given sectional properties, laid at a gradient. This is discussed in Chapter 9. Here, our main concern will be the computation of flow profiles for channels of elementary shapes. In the idealized situation, considered in the previous section, it has been possible to express the depth of flow as an explicit function of x, and the graph of this function gives the flow profile.

Referring to Eq. (7.1), the numerator of the expression on the right-hand side is zero at the upstream end, for there is no flow. Since, the denominator is not zero there, the flow profile at the upstream end is horizontal. Furthermore, since the second derivative of y is negative, the depth of flow at the upstream end is maximum. This is true also in the case of a real, horizontally laid channel where, although, friction dominates the flow, due to no velocity at the upstream end, the friction slope S_f is identically zero. With the introduction of a gradient, the point of maximum depth tends to move downstream, and the analysis shows that, for a given channel, there is a certain gradient at which the maximum depth is at the downstream end. At steeper gradients, the characteristic feature of the flow profile, in which the tangent to the water surface, at maximum depth, is parallel to the channel bed is lost, although the depth of flow at the downstream end remains more than anywhere else in the channel.

Despite the limitation of the solution of the idealised equation of the varied flow, it can be used in the design of roof gutters which are of short length, so that friction is less significant, and are laid nearly level. But, for lengths longer than 50 times the overall depth, the reduction in the capacity of the gutter due to friction becomes significant (see BS 6367). In a real-life situation, friction has to be considered from the start, and the design must be based on the solution of Eq. (3.15).

Due to the lack of an exact solution of Eq. (3.15), the varied flow has to be treated either by the computational fluid dynamics (CFD), or by application of the well-known step method. The former approach is not generally accessible to the average engineer, and is also beyond the scope of this book.

It is therefore considered appropriate to focus on the latter approach, which will be shown to yield reasonably accurate results for many practical problems. The two methods that are applied in this book are (*a*) the Newton-Raphson method (see Appendix A), and (*b*) the Runge-Kutta method (see Appendix B).

7.3 Solution of the varied flow equation by the step method

It has been pointed out that the equation of the step method, Eq. (3.17), relates the properties at the ends of an arbitrarily chosen step length of flow. Hence, as is common with numerical methods for solving problems in other areas, the step method starts at a cross section where all necessary hydraulic properties are known. Such a cross section of flow is referred to as the *control section*.

In the majority of cases of practical interest, there is a *free outfall* at the end of the channel where the specific energy of flow is minimum (in the mathematical sense), and the depth of flow critical, that is, independent of the channel gradient. In such cases, the downstream end of the channel will act as a control section of which the hydraulic properties can be derived from the depth of flow. However, for any arbitrary set of section properties and the gradient of a channel, the downstream end may not necessarily be the control section, for it can be shown that, given the geometry of the cross section, the flow at the downstream end is critical only up to a certain gradient. At other gradients, the control section will be located elsewhere within the reach and, in extreme cases of gradients, it will be almost at the upstream end, the flow in the entire channel becoming super-critical. Since a discussion on the exact location of the control section is deferred to the following chapter, it is assumed here that the location of the control section is known, and focus is on the development of the step method leading to the computation of flow profiles.

In the following analysis, the distance along the channel is measured from the upstream end, and the solution step extends from the control section, say, at $x = x_0$ to a neighbouring cross section $x = x_0 + \delta x$ (see Fig. 7.1). Accordingly, Eq. (3.17)

$$\frac{1}{g}(Q_b U_b - Q_a U_a) - \frac{1}{2}S_0(A_a + A_b)\delta x + \frac{1}{2}(A_a S_{fa} + A_b S_{fb})\delta x$$

$$+ \frac{1}{2}(A_b + A_a)(y_b - y_a) = 0 \tag{3.17}$$

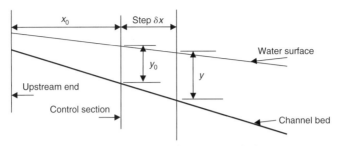

Figure 7.1 *Diagram showing particulars of the step method.*

is written as

$$\frac{1}{g}(QU - Q_0U_0) - \frac{1}{2}S_0(A_0 + A)\delta x + \frac{1}{2}(A_0S_{f0} + AS_f)\delta x$$

$$+ \frac{1}{2}(A + A_0)(y - y_0) = 0 \tag{7.12}$$

By virtue of the control section located at $x = x_0$, the properties there are known. These properties are also indicated by the suffix 0. The properties at the neighbouring cross section are without suffix, and their magnitudes can be determined only when Eq. (7.12) is solved for y. Introducing the average values

$$\overline{S}_f = \frac{AS_f + A_0S_{f0}}{A + A_0} \approx \frac{1}{2}(S_f + S_{f0}) \tag{7.13}$$

$$\overline{A} = \frac{1}{2}(A + A_0) \tag{7.14}$$

Eq. (7.12) is written as

$$\frac{1}{g}(QU - Q_0U_0) + \overline{S}_f\overline{A}\delta x - S_0\overline{A}\delta x + (y - y_0)\overline{A} = 0 \tag{7.15}$$

which is in the form suitable for the application of the Newton-Raphson method. In common with previous applications of the method, the expression on the left-hand side of this equation is represented by $F(y)$.

Since the computation starts at the control section, it is natural to accept the initial trial value of y as y_0, which is the critical depth of flow corresponding to the discharge rate $Q_0 = Q_{max}x_0/L$. The trial value of y, and the arbitrary step length δx, determine the right-hand side of Eq. (7.15) except for the unknown y.

The value of y is improved from y_0 to y_1 by adding δy to y_0 where

$$\delta y = -\left(\frac{F(y)}{dF/dy}\right)_{y=y_0} \tag{7.16}$$

From Eq. (7.15) we determine

$$\frac{dF}{dy} = \frac{1}{g}Q\frac{dU}{dy} + \left(\overline{A}\frac{d\overline{S}_f}{dy} + \overline{S}_f\frac{d\overline{A}}{dy}\right)\delta x$$

$$- S_0\frac{d\overline{A}}{dy}\delta x + (y - y_0)\frac{d\overline{A}}{dy} + \overline{A} \tag{7.17}$$

in which the derivatives are determined as follows:

$$\frac{dU}{dy} = \frac{d}{dy}\left(\frac{Q}{A}\right) = -\frac{Q}{A^2}\frac{dA}{dy} = -\frac{QT}{A^2} \tag{7.18}$$

$$\frac{d\overline{S}_f}{dy} = \overline{S}_f\left(\frac{2}{U}\frac{dU}{dy} - \frac{4}{3R}\frac{dR}{dy}\right) \tag{7.19}$$

$$\frac{dR}{dy} = \left(\frac{1}{P^2}\right)\left(P\frac{dA}{dy} - A\frac{dP}{dy}\right) \tag{7.20}$$

$$\frac{d\overline{A}}{dy} = \frac{1}{2}\frac{dA}{dy} = \frac{1}{2}T \tag{7.21}$$

The expressions for principal geometrical properties required to determine Eq. (7.16) in terms of y are given in Table 7.1.

If the control section is at the downstream end of the channel, the solution proceeds upstream. In this case, the step length δx is negative throughout the computation. If the control section is at a cross section at a distance x from the upstream end such that $0 < x < L$, L being the channel length, then the solution has two routes to follow, one leading to the profile upstream of the control section with negative δx, and the other to the profile downstream with positive δx.

Table 7.1 *Geometrical properties of elementary sections*

Property	Rectangular	Triangular	Trapezoidal	Circular*
T	B	$(m_1+m_2)y$	$B+(m_1+m_2)y$	$d \sin \theta$
P	$B+2y$	$\left(\sqrt{1+m_1^2}+\sqrt{1+m_2^2}\right)y$	$B+\left(\sqrt{1+m_1^2}+\sqrt{1+m_2^2}\right)y$	$d\theta$
A	By	$0 \cdot 5(m_1+m_2)y^2$	$By+0 \cdot 5(m_1+m_2)y^2$	$0 \cdot 25d^2(\theta - \sin \theta \cos \theta)$
dP/dy	2	$\sqrt{1+m_1^2}+\sqrt{1+m_2^2}$	$\sqrt{1+m_1^2}+\sqrt{1+m_2^2}$	$2\,\mathrm{cosec}\,\theta$

* d is the diameter of the pipe.

7.4 Convergence and accuracy of the solution by the step method

Relating to the convergence of the solution, there are two aspects of the step method, namely, the convergence of the value of y at the end of each step, and the accuracy of the computed flow profile. The solution for y is said to converge if, after a certain number of iterations, the magnitude of the correction δy is found to be less than a pre-assigned *tolerance value*, say, 10^{-3} to 10^{-5} m (see Example 7.3).

The following example of a rectangular channel, which is taken from reference [7.1], illustrates the working of the step method. It will be taken up again as Example 7.4 of the computation of the flow profiles over a range of gradients. Again, later in Chapter 8, it will be used to illustrate the method for locating the control section for a specified channel gradient.

Example 7.3: A rectangular channel 150 mm wide is laid at zero gradient. The channel carries rainwater discharge from a 40 m wide pavement over which the intensity of rainfall is 40 mm/hr. If the length of the channel is 50 m, find the depth of flow at 0·5 m from the downstream end. Manning's n is 0·015.

Solution: Assuming the runoff coefficient as 1·0, the discharge at the outlet is given by

$$Q = \frac{40{\cdot}0 \times 50{\cdot}0 \times 40{\cdot}0}{3600} = 22{\cdot}22 \, \text{l/s}$$

Since the channel has zero gradient, the control section is at the downstream end. Hence,

$$x_0 = 50 \, \text{m}$$

Therefore,

$$Q_0 = 0{\cdot}02222 \, \text{m}^3/\text{s}$$

$$y_0 = y_c = \sqrt[3]{\frac{1}{9{\cdot}806}\left(\frac{0{\cdot}02222}{0{\cdot}15}\right)^2} = 0{\cdot}1308 \, \text{m}$$

$$A_0 = 0{\cdot}15 \times 0{\cdot}1308 = 0{\cdot}01962 \, \text{m}^2$$

$$P_0 = 0{\cdot}15 + 0{\cdot}2616 = 0{\cdot}4116 \, \text{m}$$

$$R_0 = \frac{A_0}{P_0} = \frac{0{\cdot}01962}{0{\cdot}4116} = 0{\cdot}04767 \, \text{m}$$

$$U_0 = \frac{Q_0}{A_0} = \frac{0{\cdot}02222}{0{\cdot}01962} = 1{\cdot}1325 \text{ m/s}$$

$$S_{f0} = \frac{n^2 U_0^2}{R_0^{4/3}} = \frac{(0{\cdot}015 \times 1{\cdot}1325)^2}{(0{\cdot}04767)^{4/3}} = 0{\cdot}0167$$

In order to calculate the depth of flow at $x = 49{\cdot}5$ m, we assume a single step of length $0{\cdot}5$ m, so that

$$Q = \frac{0{\cdot}02222 \times 49{\cdot}5}{50} = 0{\cdot}022 \text{ m}^3/\text{s}$$

Iteration 1

$$y = y_0 = 0{\cdot}1308 \text{ m}$$

$$A = A_0 = 0{\cdot}01962 \text{ m}^2$$

$$P = P_0 = 0{\cdot}4116 \text{ m}$$

$$R = R_0 = 0{\cdot}04767 \text{ m}$$

$$U = \frac{Q}{A} = \frac{0{\cdot}022}{0{\cdot}01962} = 1{\cdot}1212 \text{ m/s}$$

$$S_f = \frac{n^2 U^2}{R^{4/3}} = \frac{(0{\cdot}015 \times 1{\cdot}1212)^2}{(0{\cdot}04767)^{4/3}} = 0{\cdot}0164$$

From Eq. (7.13)

$$\bar{S}_f = \frac{1}{2}(0{\cdot}0167 + 0{\cdot}0164) = 0{\cdot}01653$$

From Eq. (7.14)

$$\bar{A} = 0{\cdot}01962$$

From Eq. (7.15)

$$F(y) = \frac{1}{9{\cdot}806}[(0{\cdot}0220)(1{\cdot}1212) - (0{\cdot}02222)(1{\cdot}1325)]$$

$$- (0{\cdot}01653)(0{\cdot}01962)(0{\cdot}5)$$

$$= -0{\cdot}00005039 - 0{\cdot}000162 = -0{\cdot}000212$$

From Eqs (7.16) to (7.20)

$$\frac{dU}{dy} = -\left(\frac{0\cdot02220}{0\cdot01962^2}\right) \times 0\cdot15 = -8\cdot5727$$

$$\frac{dR}{dy} = \left(\frac{1}{0\cdot4116^2}\right)(0\cdot4116 \times 0\cdot15 - 0\cdot01962 \times 2) = 0\cdot1328$$

$$\frac{d\overline{S}_f}{dy} = 0\cdot01653\left(-\frac{2 \times 8\cdot5727}{1\cdot1212} - \frac{4 \times 0\cdot1328}{3 \times 0\cdot04767}\right) = -0\cdot3142$$

$$\left(\frac{dF}{dy}\right)_{y_0} = -\frac{0\cdot0220 \times 8\cdot5727}{9\cdot806}$$

$$+ (-0\cdot01962 \times 0\cdot3142 + 0\cdot01653 \times 0\cdot075)(0\cdot5) + 0\cdot01962$$

$$= -0\cdot01923 - (-0\cdot00616 + 0\cdot00124)(0\cdot5) + 0\cdot01962 = 0\cdot00285$$

$$\delta y = \frac{0\cdot000212}{0\cdot00285} = 0\cdot0744\,\text{m}$$

Therefore,

$$y = 0\cdot1308 + 0\cdot0744 = 0\cdot2052\,\text{m} = 205\cdot2\,\text{mm}$$

The solution converges after 5 iterations to $y = 161\cdot6$ mm. The following are the computed values of y:

Iteration	y (mm)
1	205·2
2	173·4
3	163·7
4	161·8
5	161·6
6	161·6

The accuracy of the flow profile itself depends on the assumed length of the step; the smaller the step, the more accurate is the profile. The application

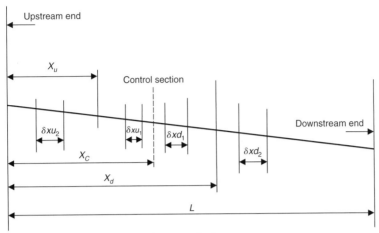

Figure 7.2 *Solution parameters of step method.*

of a fast digital computer allows the use of smaller steps, thus ensuring that the computed flow profile gives a channel length that is accurate to within a few millimetres. Furthermore, it can be demonstrated that, if the step length is reduced, the solution converges to a smaller depth of flow. The majority of results presented in Chapter 9 are based on step lengths of 1/100 of the channel length. A recommended procedure is to divide the length of the channel into segments of appropriate lengths, shorter near the control section, and longer away from it. For instance, one can select the necessary *solution parameters* similar to those shown in Fig. 7.2, where

$$X_C = \text{distance of the control section from the upstream end}$$
$$X_d - X_C = \text{segment of length downstream of the control section}$$
$$\text{divided into steps of shorter length}$$
$$X_C - X_u = \text{segment of length upstream of the control section}$$
$$\text{divided into steps of shorter length}$$
$$\delta xd_1 = \text{shorter step length in the region } L - X_d$$
$$\delta xu_1 = \text{shorter step length in the region } X_C - X_u$$
$$\delta xd_2 = \text{longer step length in the region } X_d < x \leqslant L$$
$$\delta xu_2 = \text{longer step length in the region } 0 < x \leqslant X_C$$

When the control section is very close to the upstream end, the profile upstream of the control section can be ignored, so that only the profile downstream of the control section needs to be considered. The flow in this situation will be super-critical in almost the entire channel. In the following section, the step method is applied to several examples of practical significance.

7.5 Computation of flow profiles for channels of elementary shapes

It has been pointed out that commercially available linear drainage systems may have shapes other than those classified as elementary, rectangular or circular, for instance. However, in order to illustrate the procedure for computing a flow profile, it is appropriate to begin with such sections. Let us begin with the example of a rectangular channel.

In each example considered in sequel, the following data is assumed to be known:

Channel dimensions
Length of channel (L)
Maximum discharge (Q_{max}), or rate of inflow ($q_i = Q_{max}/L$)
Channel gradient (S_0)
Manning's n

7.5.1 Rectangular channel

Example 7.4:

$B = 0.15\,m$
$L = 50.0\,m$
$q_i = 0.4444\,l/s/m$
$S_0 = 0.0\%, 0.5\%, 1.0\%, 2.0\%, 4.0\%$ and 10.0%
$n = 0.015$

Solution:
At gradients 0.0% to 2.0%, the control section is located at the downstream end, and the solution parameters for the upstream profile only are required. At these gradients, the depth of flow at the outlet is $0.1308\,m$ (see Example 7.3).

At gradients of 4.0% and 10.0%, the location of the control section should be determined by the procedure discussed in Chapter 8. It will be found that control sections at these gradients are located at $X_C = 0.4\,m$, and $X_C = 0.02\,m$, respectively, and the corresponding depths of flow are determined as follows:

$S_0 = 4.0\%$
$x = 0.4\,m$

$$Q = \frac{0.4 \times 22.22}{50.0} = 0.1778\,l/s$$

$$y = \left[\frac{1}{g}\left(\frac{Q}{B}\right)^2\right]^{1/3} = \left[\frac{1}{9.806}\left(\frac{0.1778 \times 10^{-3}}{0.15}\right)^2\right]^{1/3} = 5.23 \text{ mm}$$

$S_0 = 10.0\%$
$x = 0.02 \text{ m}$

$$Q = \frac{0.02 \times 22.22}{50.0} = 8.889 \times 10^{-3} \text{ l/s}$$

$$y = \left[\frac{1}{9.806}\left(\frac{8.889 \times 10^{-6}}{0.15}\right)^2\right]^{1/3} = 0.71 \text{ mm}$$

The depths of flow, upstream of the control sections at gradients of 4·0% and 10·0%, are very small, and the flow at such small depths is only academic, but the determination of the depth at the control sections assists the computation of the profile as a continuous curve. The depths are computed on the basis of the solution parameters shown in Table 7.2, and a tolerance of 0·01 mm. Their values are given in Table 7.3. The profiles are shown in Fig. 7.3. The table also contains the Froude numbers to indicate the nature of flow in the channel.

7.5.2 Triangular channel

Example 7.5:

$m_1 = 1.0 \qquad m_2 = 5.0$
$L = 130.0 \text{ m}$
$Q_{max} = 14.977 \text{ l/s}$
$S_0 = 0.0\%, 1.0\% \text{ and } 2.0\%$
$n = 0.013$

At 0·0% gradient, the control section is located at the downstream end, and the solution parameters for the upstream profile only are required. The corresponding depth of flow at the outlet is given by Eq. (6.11)

$$y = \left(\frac{2Q_{max}^2}{m^2 g}\right)^{1/5} = \left[\frac{2}{9.806}\left(\frac{14.977 \times 10^{-3}}{3}\right)^2\right]^{1/5} = 0.0873 \text{ m}$$

Table 7.2 *Solution parameters used for Example 7.4 (rectangular channel)*

Gradient	$S_0 \leqslant 2 \cdot 0\%$	4·0%	10·0%
X_C	50·0	0·40	0·020
X_d	–	2·00	2·000
X_u	45·0	0·30	0·300
δxd_1	–	0·10	0·100
δxd_2	–	1·00	1·000
δxu_1	−0·5	−0·05	−0·0025
δxu_2	−1·0	−0·05	−0·0025

Table 7.3 *Flow profiles for the rectangular channel of Example 7.4 gradients 0·0%, 2.0% and 10·0% (see also Fig. 7.3)*

x (m)	Depth of flow y (mm) and Froude numbers					
	$S_0 = 0 \cdot 0\%$		$S_0 = 2 \cdot 0\%$		$S_0 = 10 \cdot 0\%$	
	y	F	y	F	y	F
2·0	290·7	0·006	17·9	0·492	8·8	2·29
4·0	290·6	0·024	26·2	0·892	13·3	2·46
6·0	290·3	0·036	33·2	0·939	17·1	2·54
8·0	289·9	0·049	39·5	0·965	20·4	2·59
10·0	289·4	0·061	45·3	0·980	23·5	2·62
20·0	283·6	0·125	71·1	0·998	36·8	2·68
30·0	270·3	0·202	94·1	0·983	48·3	2·67
40·0	242·5	0·317	115·8	0·960	59·0	2·64
45·0	216·0	0·424	126·4	0·948	64·1	2·62
48·0	188·2	0·556	132·6	0·940	67·1	2·61
49·0	172·9	0·645	134·8	0·937	68·1	2·61
50·0	130·8	1·000	130·8	1·000	69·1	2·60

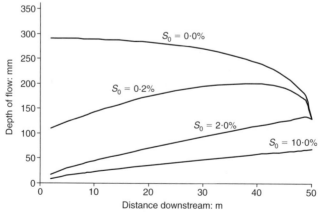

Figure 7.3 *Flow profiles for the rectangular channel of Example 7.4.*

At gradients of 1·0% and 2·0%, the control sections are found to be located at $X_C = 12·0\,\text{m}$, and $X_C = 1·4\,\text{m}$, respectively, and the corresponding depths of flow are determined as follows:

$S_0 = 1·0\%$
$x = 12·0\,\text{m}$

$$Q = \frac{12·0 \times 14·977}{130·0} = 1·3825\,\text{l/s}$$

$$y = \left(\frac{2Q^2}{m^2 g}\right)^{1/5} = \left[\frac{2}{9·806}\left(\frac{1·3825 \times 10^{-3}}{3}\right)^2\right]^{1/5} = 0·0337\,\text{m}$$

$S_0 = 2·0\%$
$x = 1·4\,\text{m}$

$$Q = \frac{1·4 \times 14·977}{130·0} = 0·16129\,\text{l/s}$$

$$y = \left(\frac{2Q^2}{m^2 g}\right)^{1/5} = \left[\frac{2}{9·806}\left(\frac{0·16129 \times 10^{-3}}{3}\right)^2\right]^{1/5} = 0·01426\,\text{m}$$

The depths are computed on the basis of the solution parameters shown in Table 7.4, and a tolerance of 0·01 mm. The depths of flow are given in Table 7.5.

Table 7.4 *Solution parameters used for Example 7.5 (triangular channel)*

Gradient	0·0%	1·0%	2·0%
X_C	130·0	10·0	1·50
X_d	–	20·0	20·00
X_u	100·0	5·0	–
$\delta x d_1$	–	1·0	1·0
$\delta x d_2$	–	5·0	5·0
$\delta x u_1$	−1·0	−1·0	–
$\delta x u_2$	−5·0	−1·0	–

Table 7.5 *Flow profiles for the triangular channel of Example 7.5*

x (m)	Depth of flow y (mm)		
	$S_0 = 0 \cdot 0\%$	$S_0 = 1 \cdot 0\%$	$S_0 = 2 \cdot 0\%$
5·0	146·5	24·9	21·4
10·0	146·5	31·3	27·2
15·0	146·4	36·7	31·4
20·0	146·3	40·1	34·8
30·0	146·0	46·3	40·1
40·0	145·6	51·3	44·6
50·0	144·8	55·6	48·5
60·0	143·8	59·4	51·8
70·0	142·3	62·8	54·8
80·0	140·4	65·9	57·6
90·0	137·7	68·8	60·1
100·0	134·4	71·5	62·5
110·0	129·1	74·1	64·7
120·0	120·5	76·5	66·8
130·0	87·3	78·7	68·8

7.5.3 Trapezoidal channel

Example 7.6:

$B = 0 \cdot 15 \, \text{m}$ $m_1 = m_2 = 0 \cdot 5$ $L = 50 \cdot 0 \, \text{m}$
Width of area to be drained $= 50 \cdot 0 \, \text{m}$
Intensity of rainfall $= 40 \cdot 0 \, \text{mm/hr}$
$S_0 = 0 \cdot 0\%, 5 \cdot 0\%, 10 \cdot 0\%$ and $30 \cdot 0\%$
$n = 0 \cdot 015$

Solution:
At gradients of 0.0%, the control section is located at the downstream end where the depth of flow, obtained numerically, is $0 \cdot 1303 \, \text{m}$. The accuracy of this value is checked as follows:

$$T = 0 \cdot 15 + 0 \cdot 1303 = 0 \cdot 2803 \, \text{m}$$

$$A = \frac{1}{2}(0 \cdot 2803 + 0 \cdot 15)(0 \cdot 1303) = 0 \cdot 02803 \, \text{m}^2$$

$$D = \frac{A}{T} = \frac{0 \cdot 02803}{0 \cdot 2803} = 0 \cdot 1 \, \text{m}$$

$$Q = \frac{50 \cdot 0 \times 50 \cdot 0 \times 40 \cdot 0}{3600} = 27 \cdot 78 \, \text{l/s}$$

$$U = \frac{Q}{A} = \frac{27 \cdot 78}{0 \cdot 02803} = 0 \cdot 9911 \, \text{m/s}$$

Therefore,

$$F = \frac{U^2}{gD} = \frac{0 \cdot 9911^2}{9 \cdot 806 \times 0 \cdot 1} = 1 \cdot 0$$

This verifies that the flow at the downstream end is critical.

The location of the control sections and the corresponding critical depths of flow are as follows:

S_0 (%)	X_C (m)	y_c (mm)
0	50·0	130·3
2	5·0	31·53
3	1·0	11·05
5	0·1	2·4

The flow profiles are shown in Table 7.6.

Table 7.6 *Flow profiles for the trapezoidal channel of Example 7.6*

x (m)	Depth of flow y (mm)			
	$S_0 = 0 \cdot 0\%$	$S_0 = 2 \cdot 0\%$	$S_0 = 3 \cdot 0\%$	$S_0 = 5 \cdot 0\%$
2·0	232·4	20·4	16·9	13·3
4·0	232·3	29·1	24·0	19·4
6·0	232·1	34·5	29·7	24·4
8·0	231·8	41·0	34·8	28·7
10·0	231·5	46·4	39·4	32·6
20·0	227·8	67·6	58·2	48·6
30·0	219·7	84·4	73·1	61·5
40·0	203·1	98·7	86·0	72·6
45·0	187·0	105·3	91·9	77·7
48·0	169·7	109·0	95·3	80·6
49·0	159·9	110·3	96·4	81·6
50·0	130·3	111·5	97·5	82·5

Table 7.7 *Flow profiles for the circular pipe of Example 7.7*

x (m)	Depth of flow y (mm)				
	$S_0 = 0 \cdot 0\%$	$S_0 = 1 \cdot 0\%$	$S_0 = 2 \cdot 0\%$	$S_0 = 5 \cdot 0\%$	$S_0 = 10 \cdot 0\%$
2·0	147·2	17·8	13·7	7·5	8·5
4·0	147·1	22·6	18·0	13·7	11·4
6·0	147·0	26·8	21·3	16·4	13·7
8·0	146·7	31·7	24·1	18·7	15·5
10·0	146·4	33·1	26·6	20·5	17·2
20·0	143·2	45·1	36·5	28·3	23·5
30·0	136·3	54·7	44·3	34·4	28·7
40·0	123·3	63·2	51·0	39·5	32·9
45·0	111·9	67·1	54·1	41·9	34·8
48·0	100·5	69·4	55·9	43·2	35·9
49·0	94·3	70·2	56·5	43·7	36·3
50·0	76·6	71·0	57·1	44·1	36·7

7.5.4 Circular pipe

Example 7.7:

$$d = 0 \cdot 15\,\mathrm{m}$$
$$L = 50 \cdot 0\,\mathrm{m}$$
$$Q_{max} = 7 \cdot 0\,\mathrm{l/s}$$
$$S_0 = 0 \cdot 0\%, 0 \cdot 1\%, 1 \cdot 0\%, 2 \cdot 0\% \text{ and } 10 \cdot 0\%$$
$$n = 0 \cdot 011$$

Solution:

At 0.0% and 0·1% gradients, the control section is located at the downstream end, and the solution parameters for the upstream profile only are required. The position of the control sections at other gradients are:

Gradient	1·0%	2·0%	5·0%	10·0%
X_C	9·5	1·0	0·12	0·02

The profiles are shown in Table 7.7.

7.6 Examples of flow profiles for channels of arbitrary shapes

Quite often, a drainage system consists of channels of arbitrary shapes, for instance, a U-shaped channel, or one of more complicated shape. An expedient, used in the latter situation, is to replace the channel by an *equivalent rectangular channel*, that is, one of the same cross-sectional area and height as of the original channel, thus allowing the conclusions drawn from flow profile computed for the rectangular channel to be applied to the original channel. This approach is, particularly, useful in deciding upon the capacity of the channel using the criterion that the depth of flow anywhere in the channel does not exceed the available depth of the channel. The dimensions of the rectangular channel are determined on the basis of the original channel running full, and the flow profile computed as in Example 7.4. In this section, we consider a U-shaped channel, and compute the flow profile by applying the Runge-Kutta method (see Appendix B).

In dealing with a channel, such as a U-shaped channel, in which the geometry of the cross section changes from one configuration to another, it is necessary to first establish the critical water level relative to the height at which the cross section changes. In a U-shaped channel, the critical discharge capacity, Q_{inv} of the circular invert is given by

$$Q_{inv} = A_{inv}\sqrt{gD_{inv}}$$

where A_{inv} is the area of the invert, and

$$D_{inv} = \frac{A_{inv}}{d}$$

Hence, if Q_{inv} is less than the rate of discharge at the critical section then the critical water level will be higher than the top of the invert, otherwise within it (see section 6.5.3). *In applying the step method, it is necessary to use this criterion to check the water level at each step.*

Example 7.8: A U-shaped channel shown in Fig. 7.4 is to carry a discharge from a paved area of width 20·0 m. If the design rainfall is 50 mm/hr, and

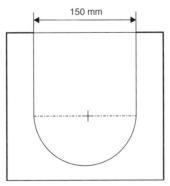

Figure 7.4 *A U-shaped linear drainage system.*

Table 7.8 *Flow profiles for the U-shaped channel of Example 7.8*

x (m)	Depth of flow y (mm)				
	$S_0 = 0 \cdot 0\%$	$S_0 = 0 \cdot 2\%$	$S_0 = 2 \cdot 0\%$	$S_0 = 3 \cdot 0\%$	$S_0 = 5 \cdot 0\%$
2·0	225·4	146·7	20·8	16·9	14·1
4·0	225·3	150·4	26·5	23·2	19·7
6·0	225·1	153·9	31·4	27·6	23·5
8·0	224·8	157·3	35·5	31·3	26·8
10·0	224·4	160·4	39·2	34·6	29·6
20·0	220·4	173·0	54·1	47·7	41·0
30·0	211·6	179·3	66·1	58·2	49·9
40·0	193·5	175·6	87·0	67·4	57·7
50·0	111·7	111·7	102·9	82·8	64·8

the length of the channel is 50 m, compute the flow profile for the channel gradients of 0·0%, 0·2%, 2·0%, 3·0%, and 5·0%.

Solution: At $S_0 = 0 \cdot 0$ and $0 \cdot 2\%$, the control section is at the downstream end of the channel, where the discharge Q_{max} is given by

$$Q_{max} = \frac{20 \cdot 0 \times 50 \cdot 0 \times 50 \cdot 0}{3600} = 13 \cdot 89 \, l/s$$

If the flow occupies just the invert

$$D = \frac{\pi d}{8} = \frac{0 \cdot 15 \pi}{8} = 0 \cdot 0589 \, m$$

hence, for the flow to be critical when it is up to the top of invert

$$U = \sqrt{gD} = \sqrt{9 \cdot 806 \times 0 \cdot 0589} = 0 \cdot 76 \, m/s$$

that is,

$$Q_{inv} = \frac{1}{8} \pi (0 \cdot 15^2) 0 \cdot 76 = 6 \cdot 72 \, l/s$$

Since this value is less than Q_{max} the water level in the channel will vary with respect to the top of the invert. If the channel is nearly level, the minimum depth of the system should be 150 mm above the top of the invert. At steeper slopes than, say, 3%, most of the flow will be confined to the invert.

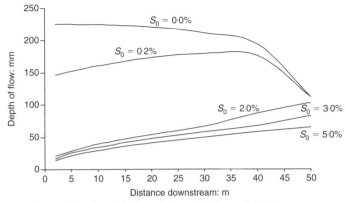

Figure 7.5 *Flow profiles for a U-shaped channel (Example 7.8).*

The distances of the control sections from the upstream end are:

Gradient	0·0%	0·2%	2·0%	3·0%	5·0%
X_C (m)	50·0	50·0	2·0	0·1	0·1

Example 7.9: Figure 7.6 shows the unit of a linear drainage system, commercially known as Beany blocks. Compute the flow profile for the system laid at various gradients from 0% to 10%. Assume the channel to be flowing full, and $n = 0\cdot011$.

Solution: From the estimated inner dimensions, which defines the cross section of flow when the channel runs full, we determine

$$A = \frac{1}{2}(150 + 280) \times 205 + \frac{1}{2}(235 + 280) \times 150$$

$$= 44\,075 + 38\,625 = 82\,700\,\text{mm}^2$$

The dimensions of the equivalent rectangular channel are to be calculated from the following measured values:

$$A = 0\cdot084\,\text{m}^2 \qquad P = 0\cdot922\,\text{m}$$

Hence, we have

$$B = 237\,\text{mm} \qquad h = 355\,\text{mm}$$

The distances of the control sections from the upstream end are:

Gradient	0·0%	0·033%	0·6%	1·0%	5·0%
X_C (m)	100·0	100·0	100·0	8·0	0·05

The profiles for the system are given in Table 7.9.

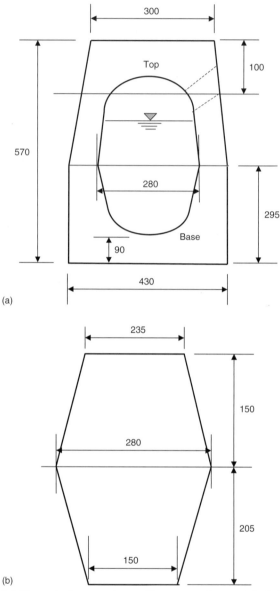

(a)

(b)

Figure 7.6 *(a) A linear drainage system with compound geometrical shape. (b) Inner dimensions (mm) of the full-flowing system (cross section of flow).*

It is interesting to note that all of the profiles are remarkably similar in pattern, that is, when the channel gradient is laid level, the maximum depth of flow occurs at the upstream end of the channel. This feature is discussed in section 7.2. However, given a small gradient, the maximum

Table 7.9 *Flow profiles for the 'Beany' system of Example 7.9*

x (m)	Depth of flow y (mm)				
	$S_0 = 0{\cdot}0\%$	$S_0 = 0{\cdot}033\%$	$S_0 = 0{\cdot}6\%$	$S_0 = 1{\cdot}0\%$	$S_0 = 10{\cdot}0\%$
10·0	204·7	181·1	25·6	19·9	11·0
20·0	204·2	182·9	37·1	29·7	17·4
30·0	203·0	184·0	48·0	38·5	20·6
40·0	200·6	184·4	57·4	45·8	26·0
50·0	197·0	183·5	66·1	53·1	29·1
60·0	191·8	180·9	74·4	59·5	33·1
70·0	184·3	176·0	82·3	66·0	36·3
80·0	173·6	167·7	90·0	72·1	39·7
90·0	156·7	153·4	97·5	78·1	42·8
100·0	94·3	94·3	94·3	83·9	45·9

depth moves rapidly downstream and, once reaching the downstream end, stays there.

Reference

[7.1] ANDERSON J.A., 'Linear Drainage Channels for Paved Surfaces', *Highways and Transportation*, March 1997.

8

Computation of varied flow II: location of control section

In solving the varied flow equation, the solution has to start at the control section. The control section is at the downstream end of a channel when the gradient increases from zero to a value dependent upon the flow configuration. When this value is exceeded, the control section moves upstream and, for a certain gradient, is located at the upstrem end of the channel. This chapter describes the method for locating the control section for various flow configurations.

8.1 General equation for location of the control section

Let the flow at some distance $x = x_c$ from the upstream end of a channel be critical. This means that, at a section $x = x_1$, where $x_1 < x_c$, the flow is sub-critical, and at another section $x = x_2$, where $x_2 > x_c$, the flow is super-critical. This condition is expressed by the following relationships:

$$\text{at } x = x_1; \quad \frac{U^2}{gD} < 1 \tag{8.1}$$

$$\text{at } x = x_c; \quad \frac{U^2}{gD} = 1 \tag{8.2}$$

$$\text{at } x = x_2; \quad \frac{U^2}{gD} > 1 \tag{8.3}$$

We now apply the principle that, for a smooth transfer of energy from one cross section of flow to the next, the flow profile must have a continuously turning tangent, that is, at $x = x_c$, dy/dx must be finite. Since the denominator of Eq. (3.15)

$$\frac{dy}{dx} = \frac{S_0 - S_f - (2Q/gA^2)(dQ/dx)}{1 - (Q^2/gA^2D)} \tag{3.15}$$

at $x = x_c$ is zero,

$$U^2 = \frac{Q^2}{A^2} = gD$$

that is,

$$Q^2 = \frac{gA^3}{T} \tag{8.4}$$

we must also have

$$S_0 - S_f = \frac{2Q(dQ/dx)}{gA^2} \tag{8.5}$$

Assuming that the discharge varies linearly with x, and that there is no lateral inflow at $x = 0$, we have

$$\frac{dQ}{dx} = \frac{Q}{x} = q_i \tag{8.6}$$

where q_i is the rate of inflow, assumed to be constant. With this substitution into Eq. (8.5), we find that the flow at a distance x from the upstream end is critical if the following equation is satisfied:

$$S_0 - S_f = \frac{2q_i^2 x}{gA^2} \tag{8.7}$$

We also obtain from Eq. (8.4)

$$A^2 = \frac{Q^{4/3}T^{2/3}}{g^{2/3}} = \frac{q_i^{4/3}x^{4/3}T^{2/3}}{g^{2/3}}$$

Substitution of this into Eq. (8.7) gives

$$S_0 - S_f = \frac{2q_i^{2/3}}{g^{1/3}T^{2/3}x^{1/3}}$$

that is,

$$x = \frac{8q_i^2}{gT^2(S_0 - S_f)^3} \tag{8.8}$$

This equation determines the position of the control section for a specified channel gradient S_0. It is to be noted that, due to the presence of the variable friction slope S_f on the right-hand side, Eq. (8.8) is not amenable to exact solution, and resort is taken to a numerical approach. However, before a numerical solution of Eq. (8.8) can be constructed, we attempt to answer in the next section the following question: Given a location x of the control section, what is the channel gradient? The answer to this question leads to a table containing channel gradients corresponding to various locations of the control section. From this table, the required location of the control section is determined by using one of the following methods:

(a) Select a value of x that corresponds to a gradient close to the specified gradient, and refine the value by, say, the Newton-Raphson method.
(b) Determine x, by inspection, or by interpolation.

8.2 Gradients corresponding to an arbitrary location of the control section

Let the gradient of the channel corresponding to the control section at a distance x from the upstream end be $S_{0,x}$. After an adjustment of terms, Eq. (8.8) becomes

$$S_{0,x} = S_{f,x} + 2\left(\frac{q_i^2}{gT_{c,x}^2 x}\right)^{1/3} \tag{8.9}$$

where $T_{c,x}$ and $S_{f,x}$ are the 'local' values of the top width T, and the friction slope S_f, respectively. The friction slope is obtained from Eq. (3.11)

$$S_f = \frac{n^2Q^2}{A^2R^{4/3}} \tag{3.11}$$

in which Q^2/A^2 is to be replaced by $gD_{c,x}$, where $D_{c,x}$ is the local value of the hydraulic depth. Hence, we have

$$S_{f,x} = \frac{n^2gD_{c,x}}{R_{c,x}^{4/3}} \tag{8.10}$$

Also, since the flow at x is critical,

$$\frac{q_i^2}{gT_{c,x}^2 x} = \frac{Q^2}{gT_{c,x}^2 x^3} = \frac{U_{c,x}^2 A_{c,x}^2}{gT_{c,x}^2 x^3} = \frac{U_{c,x}^2 D_{c,x}^2}{gx^3} = \frac{D_{c,x}^3}{x^3}$$

Hence, Eq. (8.9) becomes

$$S_{0,x} = S_{f,x} + 2\frac{D_{c,x}}{x} \tag{8.11}$$

When the critical section coincides with the downstream end, $x = L$, we have the corresponding gradient $S_{0,L}$ given by

$$S_{0,L} = S_{f,L} + 2\frac{D_{c,L}}{L} \tag{8.12}$$

where $S_{f,L}$ and $D_{c,L}$ are, respectively, the friction slope and the hydraulic depth at $x = L$.

This leads to the following procedure for determining the channel gradient $S_{0,x}$ at an arbitrary location x of the critical section:

(a) From the given rate of lateral inflow q_i, determine the rate of longitudinal flow Q: $Q = q_i x$.
(b) Determine $y_{c,x}$, either exactly (section 6.4), or numerically (section 6.5).
(c) Determine $D_{c,x}$ and $R_{c,x}$.
(d) Determine $S_{f,x}$ from Eq. (8.10).
(e) Determine $S_{0,x}$ from Eq. (8.11).

The treatment of triangular or rectangular channels in the light of Eq. (8.11) is more direct, which reveals some interesting aspects associated with the location of the control section.

8.2.1 Triangular channel

Similar to Eq. (8.10), is the equation for the friction slope at the downstream end of the channel:

$$S_{f,L} = \frac{n^2 g D_{c,L}}{R_{c,L}^{4/3}} \tag{8.13}$$

Introducing the ratio

$$\overline{S}_{f,x} = \frac{S_{f,x}}{S_{f,L}} \tag{8.14}$$

and combining Eqs (8.10) and (8.13), and we obtain

$$\bar{S}_{f,x} = \frac{D_{c,x}\,(R_{c,L})^{4/3}}{D_{c,L}\,(R_{c,x})^{4/3}} \tag{8.15}$$

Substitution of expressions for $D_{c,x}$, $D_{c,L}$, $R_{c,x}$ and $R_{c,L}$ from Eqs (2.6d) and (2.6e), into this equation, and simplification results in

$$\bar{S}_{f,x} = \left(\frac{y_{c,x}}{y_{c,L}}\right)^{-1/3} \tag{8.16}$$

Applying the relationship $Q = q_i x$, and recalling Eq. (6.11)

$$y_c = \left(\frac{2Q^2}{gm^2}\right)^{1/5} \tag{6.11}$$

which gives

$$y_{c,x} = \left(\frac{2q_i^2}{gm^2}\right)^{1/5} x^{2/5}$$

for any x, we obtain

$$\frac{y_{c,x}}{y_{c,L}} = \left(\frac{x}{L}\right)^{2/5} \tag{8.17}$$

When this is substituted into Eq. (8.16), the result is

$$\bar{S}_{f,x} = \left(\frac{x}{L}\right)^{-2/15} \tag{8.18}$$

According to this equation, the friction slope increases when the control section moves upstream. Applying the relationship

$$D_{c,x} = \frac{1}{2} y_{c,x}$$

for a triangular channel, we obtain from Eq. (8.11)

$$S_{0,x} = S_{f,x} + \frac{x^{-3/5}}{L^{2/5}} y_{c,L} \tag{8.19}$$

This equation shows that the difference between $S_{0,x}$ and $S_{f,x}$ also increases as the control section comes nearer to the upstream end. As a result, the associated channel gradient also increases.

Example 8.1: A triangular channel 200 m long, with side slopes $m_1 = 1 \cdot 0$, $m_2 = 5 \cdot 0$, carries a discharge which increases linearly at the rate of 0·1152 l/s/m. If the control section coincides with the downstream end of the channel, determine the associated gradient. Take Manning's $n = 0 \cdot 013$.

Solution:
At the downstream end

$$Q = 200 \times 0 \cdot 1152 = 23 \cdot 04 \, \text{l/s}$$

For a triangular channel

$$y_{c,L} = \left[\frac{8Q^2}{(m_1 + m_2)^2 g} \right]^{1/5} = \left[\frac{8 \times 0 \cdot 02304^2}{36 \cdot 0 \times 9 \cdot 806} \right]^{1/5} = 0 \cdot 1038 \, \text{m}$$

$$A_{c,L} = \frac{1}{2}(m_1 + m_2)y_{c,L}^2 = 3 \times 0 \cdot 1038^2 = 0 \cdot 0323 \, \text{m}^2$$

$$D_{c,L} = \frac{1}{2}y_{c,L} = 0 \cdot 0519 \, \text{m}$$

$$P_{c,L} = \left(\sqrt{1 + m_1^2} + \sqrt{1 + m_2^2} \right) y_{c,L}$$

$$= \left(\sqrt{2} + \sqrt{26} \right) \times 0 \cdot 1038 = 0 \cdot 6761 \, \text{m}$$

$$R_{c,L} = \frac{A_{c,L}}{P_{c,L}} = \frac{0 \cdot 0323}{0 \cdot 6761} = 0 \cdot 0478 \, \text{m}, \quad \text{giving } R_{c,L}^{4/3} = 0 \cdot 01734$$

From Eq. (8.13)

$$S_{f,L} = \frac{n^2 g D_{c,L}}{R_{c,L}^{4/3}} = \frac{(0 \cdot 013)^2 (9 \cdot 806)(0 \cdot 0519)}{0 \cdot 01734}$$

$$= 0 \cdot 00496 = 0 \cdot 496\%$$

From Eq. (8.12)

$$S_{0,L} = S_{f,L} + 2\frac{D_{c,L}}{L} = 0.00496 + \frac{2(0.0519)}{200} = 0.00548$$

$$= 0.548\%$$

Let us now apply Eq. (8.11) to various locations of the control section in the triangular channel of the above example. This leads to the generation of Table 8.1 and Fig. 8.1, which show that both friction slope and the channel gradient increase as the distance of the control section from the upstream end of the channel decreases. From these data, we also derive the following ranges of gradients of special significance:

- For the control section at the downstream end, $0.0\% \leqslant S_0 \leqslant 0.548\%$.
- For an upstream location of the control section, $S_0 > 0.548\%$.
- When the control section is very close to the upstream end, (within, say, 4 meters), $S_0 > 1.4\%$. The channel gradient continues to rise rapidly as the control section approaches the upstream end asymptotically.

8.2.2   Rectangular channel

For a rectangular channel, Eq. (8.15) translates into

$$\overline{S}_{f,x} = \frac{y_{c,x}}{y_{c,L}} \left[\frac{(y_{c,L})(B + 2y_{c,x})}{(y_{c,x})(B + 2y_{c,L})} \right]^{4/3}$$

Table 8.1 *Gradients to various locations of control section (triangular channel of Example 8.1); x = distance of control section from the upstream end; S_f = friction slope; S_0 = bed slope*

x (m)	S_f (%)	S_0 (%)	x (m)	S_f (%)	S_0 (%)
200	0.496	0.548	20	0.674	0.880
180	0.503	0.558	18	0.683	0.903
160	0.511	0.570	16	0.694	0.930
140	0.520	0.584	14	0.707	0.963
120	0.531	0.601	12	0.721	1.002
100	0.544	0.622	10	0.739	1.052
80	0.560	0.650	8	0.761	1.119
60	0.582	0.689	6	0.791	1.217
40	0.614	0.751	4	0.835	1.378
20	0.674	0.880	2	0.916	1.738

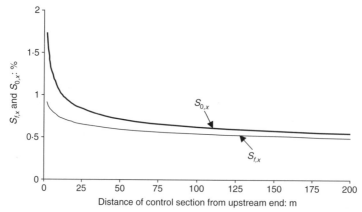

Figure 8.1 *Channel gradient and friction slopes at control sections (triangular channel).*

that is,

$$\overline{S}_{f,x} = \left(\frac{y_{c,x}}{y_{c,L}}\right)^{-1/3} \left[\frac{B + 2y_{c,x}}{B + 2y_{c,L}}\right]^{4/3} \tag{8.20}$$

Again, using the relationship $Q = q_i x$, we obtain from Eq. (6.8)

$$\frac{y_{c,x}}{y_{c,L}} = \left(\frac{x}{L}\right)^{2/3} \tag{8.21}$$

When this is substituted into Eq. (8.20), the result is

$$\overline{S}_{f,x} = \left[G_1\left(\frac{x}{L}\right)^{-1/6} + G_2\left(\frac{x}{L}\right)^{1/2}\right]^{4/3} \tag{8.22}$$

where

$$G_1 = \frac{B}{B + 2y_{c,L}} \tag{8.23}$$

$$G_2 = \frac{2y_{c,L}}{B + 2y_{c,L}} \tag{8.24}$$

From Eq. (8.22) we obtain

$$\frac{d\bar{S}_{f,x}}{dx} = \frac{4}{3L}\left[\frac{1}{2}G_2\left(\frac{x}{L}\right)^{-1/2} - \frac{1}{6}G_1\left(\frac{x}{L}\right)^{-7/6}\right]g\left(\frac{x}{L}\right) \tag{8.25}$$

where

$$g\left(\frac{x}{L}\right) = \sqrt[3]{f\left(\frac{x}{L}\right)}$$

$$f\left(\frac{x}{L}\right) = \left[G_1\left(\frac{x}{L}\right)^{-1/6} + G_2\left(\frac{x}{L}\right)^{1/2}\right] \tag{8.26}$$

Introducing the notation

$$f_1\left(\frac{x}{L}\right) = \frac{1}{2}G_2\left(\frac{x}{L}\right)^{-1/2}$$

$$f_2\left(\frac{x}{L}\right) = \frac{1}{6}G_1\left(\frac{x}{L}\right)^{-7/6}$$

we find the ratio

$$\frac{f_1(x/L)}{f_2(x/L)} = 3\frac{G_2}{G_1}\left(\frac{x}{L}\right)^{2/3} \tag{8.27}$$

and derive the following law for the variation of the friction slope in a rectangular channel:

(a) The friction slope decreases when the critical section moves upstream, and continues to decrease as long as the ratio x/L satisfies the inequality

$$\frac{x}{L} > \left(\frac{G_1}{3G_2}\right)^{3/2} \tag{8.28}$$

(b) The friction slope reaches its minimum value at

$$\frac{x}{L} = \left(\frac{G_1}{3G_2}\right)^{3/2} \tag{8.29}$$

(c) The friction slope increases at

$$\frac{x}{L} < \left(\frac{G_1}{3G_2}\right)^{3/2} \tag{8.30}$$

For a rectangular channel, it is not possible to obtain a relationship for the gradient $S_{0,x}$, similar to that of a triangular channel, and the analysis depends on numerical treatment.

Reintroducing the ratio

$$\overline{S}_{f,x} = \frac{S_{f,x}}{S_{f,L}}$$

and recalling Eq. (8.21), we write Eq. (8.11) as

$$S_{0,x} = S_{f,L}\overline{S}_{f,x} + \frac{2y_{c,L}}{L}\left(\frac{x}{L}\right)^{-1/3} \tag{8.31}$$

which, when differentiated with respect to x, simplified and equated to zero, results in the following extreme condition:

$$\left[-\frac{1}{6}G_1\left(\frac{x}{L}\right)^{1/6} + \frac{1}{2}G_2\left(\frac{x}{L}\right)^{5/6}\right]\mathcal{g}\left(\frac{x}{L}\right) - \frac{1}{2}\frac{y_{c,L}}{LS_{f,L}} = 0 \tag{8.32}$$

This equation can be solved numerically by, say, the Newton-Raphson method with an initial trial value of x given by

$$x = \frac{y_{c,L}}{(G_2)^{4/3}S_{f,L}} \tag{8.33}$$

Example 8.2: For a rectangular channel with the following data, determine the gradient at which the control section coincides with the downstream end of the channel (see also Examples 7.3 and 7.4).

$$B = 0.15 \text{ m} \qquad L = 50.0 \text{ m} \qquad q_i = 0.4444 \text{ l/s/m} \qquad n = 0.015$$

Solution: From the already known values, we obtain

$$y_{c,L} = 0.1308 \text{ m} \qquad S_{f,L} = 0.0167$$

Substituting these values in the equation

$$S_{0,L} = S_{f,L} + 2 \frac{y_{c,L}}{L} \qquad (8.34)$$

which, for a rectangular channel, is derived from Eq. (8.12).
We determine

$$S_{0,L} = 0.0167 + \frac{2 \times 0.1308}{50.0} = 0.02193$$

We also have from Eqs (8.23) and (8.24)

$$G_1 = \frac{B}{B + 2y_{c,L}} = \frac{0.15}{0.15 + 2 \times 0.1308} = 0.3644$$

$$G_2 = \frac{2y_{c,L}}{B + 2y_{c,L}} = 1 - G_1 = 0.6356$$

Starting with a trial value given by Eq. (8.33), that is,

$$x_0 = \frac{0.1308}{(0.6356)^{4/3} \times 0.0167} = 14.33 \text{ m}$$

we find that, after 3 iterations, x converges to 17·91 m, that is, $x/L = 0.3582$.
From Eq. (8.21)

$$y_{c,x} = \left(\frac{x}{L} \right)^{2/3} y_{c,L} = (0.3582)^{2/3} \times 0.1308 = 0.0660 \text{ m}$$

The substitution of the values of x/L, G_1 and G_2 in Eq. (8.22) results in

$$\bar{S}_{f,x} = \left[G_1 \left(\frac{x}{L} \right)^{-1/6} + G_2 \left(\frac{x}{L} \right)^{1/2} \right]^{4/3}$$

$$= \left[0.3644(0.3582)^{-1/6} + 0.6356(0.3582)^{1/2} \right]^{4/3} = 0.7511$$

Therefore,

$$S_{f,x} = 0.0167 \times 0.7511 = 0.01254$$

Finally, from Eq. (8.11)

$$S_{0,x} = 0.01254 + \frac{2 \times 0.0660}{17.91} = 0.0199$$

Table 8.2 *Gradients to various locations of control section (rectangular channel of Example 8.2); x = distance of control section from the upstream end; S_f = friction slope; S_0 = bed slope*

x (m)	S_f (%)	S_0 (%)	x (m)	S_f (%)	S_0 (%)
50	1·670	2·193	1·0	1·218	3·146
40	1·552	2·116	0·9	1·234	3·231
30	1·428	2·048	0·8	1·253	3·330
20	1·295	2·005	0·7	1·276	3·447
10	1·160	2·054	0·6	1·305	3·590
5	1·109	2·237	0·5	1·342	3·770
4	1·107	2·322	0·4	1·390	4·006
3	1·114	2·450	0·3	1·460	4·339
2	1·138	2·668	0·2	1·570	4·866
1	1·218	3·145	0·1	1·794	5·946

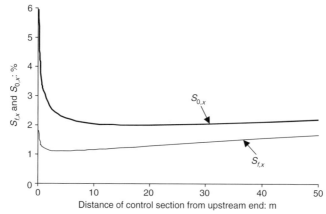

Figure 8.2 *Channel gradient and friction slopes at control sections (rectangular channel).*

The results of the application of Eq. (8.11) to the rectangular channel of the above example are shown in Table 8.2 and Fig. 8.2. From these data, the following conclusions can be drawn.

- For the control section at the downstream end, $S_0 = 2\cdot193\%$.
- When the control section is at $x = 17\cdot91$ m, the corresponding gradient is minimum at $1\cdot99\%$, which is less than the gradient at which the control section is at the downstream end, but consistent with the values given in Table 8.2. The lowering of the value of S_0 is indicated by a shallow trough in the graph in Fig. 8.2, for the gradient has to increase subsequently when the control section approaches the

upstream end. Consequently, when the channel gradient is about 2·0%, the flow and, hence, the depth of flow in almost the entire channel is critical. At steeper gradients, the location of the control section has to be determind as described in section 8.3.

8.2.3 Trapezoidal channel and circular pipe

Let us now consider a trapezoidal channel and a circular pipe through the following examples.

Example 8.3: A trapezoidal channel, 100 m long, with bottom width $B = 0·4$ m, and side slopes $m_1 = m_2 = 0·5$, carries a discharge that increases linearly at the rate of 5 l/s/m. If the control section coincides with the downstream end, determine the associated gradient. Take Manning's $n = 0·015$. Show the variation of the channel gradient at various locations of the control section.

Solution: From the procedure discussed in section 6.5.1, we determine

$$y_{c,L} = 0·4468 \text{ m}$$

from which we obtain

$$T_{c,L} = [B + (m_1 + m_2)y_{c,L}] = 0·8468 \text{ m}$$

$$A_{c,L} = \frac{1}{2}(B + T_{c,L})y_{c,L} = \frac{1}{2}(0·4 + 0·8468)0·4468 = 0·2785 \text{ m}^2$$

$$D_{c,L} = \frac{A_{c,L}}{T_{c,L}} = 0·3289 \text{ m}$$

Accuracy check:

$$U^2 = \left(\frac{0·5}{0·2785}\right)^2 = 3·223 \text{ (m/s)}^2$$

$$gD_{c,L} = 9·806 \times 0·3289 = 3·225 \text{ (m/s)}^2 \approx U^2$$

Hence, the Froude number is 1·0.

$$P_{c,L} = \left[B + \left(\sqrt{1 + m_1^2} + \sqrt{1 + m_2^2}\right)y_{c,L}\right] = 1·399 \text{ m}$$

$$R_{c,L} = \frac{A_{c,L}}{P_{c,L}} = 0·199 \text{ m},$$

that is,

$$R_{c,L}^{4/3} = 0·116$$

From Eq. (8.13)

$$S_{f,L} = \frac{n^2 g D_{c,L}}{R_{c,L}^{4/3}} = 0.00624 = 0.624\%$$

From Eq. (8.12)

$$S_{0,L} = S_{f,L} + 2\frac{D_{c,L}}{L}$$

$$= 0.00624 + \frac{2(0.3289)}{100} = 0.01282 = 1.282\%$$

Channel gradients corresponding to various locations of the control section in the above trapezoidal channel, obtained from Eq. (8.11), are shown in Fig. 8.3. Also included in Fig. 8.3 are the results obtained for channels with different side slopes. From the analysis, one can deduce that the behaviour of the friction slope is between that of a rectangular channel and a triangular channel. That is, for certain side slope–bottom width combinations, the friction slope decreases, levels off, and then increases until the control section approaches the upstream end of the channel. The channel gradient, however, continues to increase.

Example 8.4: A 100 m long, 0·15 m internal diameter, circular pipe carries a discharge that increases linearly at the rate of 0·14 l/s/m. If the control

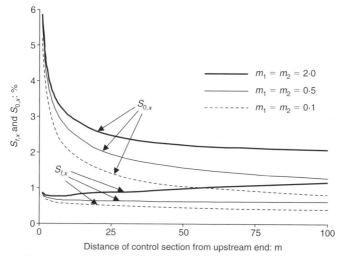

Figure 8.3 *Channel gradient and friction slopes at control sections (trapezoidal channel).*

section occurs at the downstream end, determine the associated gradient. Take Manning's $n = 0.011$.

Solution: From the procedure discussed in section 6.5.2, we determine

$$y_{c,L} = 0.11 \, \text{m}$$

which gives

$$A_{c,L} = 0.01385 \, \text{m}^2 \qquad T_{c,L} = 0.133 \, \text{m} \qquad D_{c,L} = 0.1042 \, \text{m}$$

Accuracy check:

$$U^2 = \left(\frac{0.014}{0.01385} \right)^2 = 1.0218 \, (\text{m/s})^2$$

$$gD_{c,L} = 9.806 \times 0.1042 = 1.0218 \, (\text{m/s})^2$$

Hence, the error in the computation of the critical depth is almost nil.

$$P_{c,L} = 0.308 \, \text{m} \qquad R_{c,L} = 0.045 \, \text{m}$$

From Eq. (8.13)

$$S_{f,L} = \frac{n^2 g D_{c,L}}{R_{c,L}^{4/3}} = \frac{(0.011)^2 (9.806)(0.1042)}{(0.045)^{4/3}} = 0.00772$$

From Eq. (8.12)

$$S_{0,L} = S_{f,L} + 2\frac{D_{c,L}}{L} = 0.00772 + \frac{2 \times 0.1042}{100}$$

$$= 0.00981 = 0.0981\%$$

The application of Eq. (8.11) to the above example of a circular pipe shows that, as the control section approaches the upstream end of the channel, both friction slope and channel gradients increase, but very slowly, with the increase being noticeable only when the control section is sufficiently close to the upstream end (see Fig. 8.4).

However, the channel gradient cannot increase indefinitely with the control section approaching the upstream end. For, when the critical section is 'very close' to the upstream end, the depth of flow is extremely shallow and, consequently, the flow is laminar. Furthermore, in this region of flow, the law of resistance due to turbulence, which is the assumed type of flow in drainage channels, does not apply. By limiting the Reynolds number to 2000, below which the flow is assumed to be laminar, we can determine the

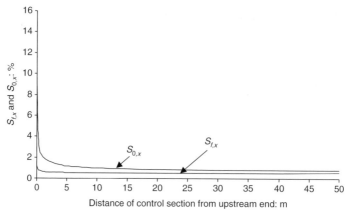

Figure 8.4 *Channel gradient and friction slopes at control sections (circular pipe).*

limiting distance from the upstream end of the channel, beyond which the flow becomes turbulent. For instance, in the case of a rectangular channel, the Reynolds number can be calculated from the formula

$$R = \frac{Uy}{v} \tag{8.35}$$

wherein

$$U = \frac{Q}{A} = \frac{q_i x}{By}$$

The substitution of this value of U in Eq. (8.35) results in

$$R = \frac{q_i x}{Bv} \tag{8.36}$$

Hence, if we apply the condition that the flow is laminar at $R < 2000$, we deduce from Eq. (8.36) the following expression for the minimum distance from the upstream end, at which the flow is turbulent:

$$x = \frac{2000Bv}{q_i} \tag{8.37}$$

As an illustration, we apply Eq. (8.37) to the rectangular channel of Example 8.2, and find that, for $v = 1{\cdot}1 \times 10^{-6}\,\mathrm{m^2/s}$

$$x = \frac{2000Bv}{q_i} = \frac{(2000)(0{\cdot}4)(1{\cdot}1 \times 10^{-6})}{0{\cdot}005} = 0{\cdot}176\ \mathrm{m}$$

8.3 Location of the control section

Having established the relationship between an arbitrary location of the control section and the associated channel gradient, the control section for a specified channel gradient can be located, either by interpolation or, alternatively, by solving Eq. (8.8) numerically. If we choose the first approach, then we need a table of gradients for a sufficient number of locations of the control section, similar to Tables 8.1 and 8.2. If, however, we use the other alternative, then we have to solve Eq. (8.8) by, say, the Newton-Raphson method (Appendix A). This requires Eq. (8.8) to be written as

$$F(x) = gT^2(S_0 - S_f)^3 x - 8q_i^2 = 0 \qquad (8.38)$$

A trial value x_0 of x is assumed, to which is added the 'correction term'

$$\delta x_0 = -\frac{F(x_0)}{F'(x_0)} \qquad (8.39)$$

where

$$
\begin{aligned}
F'(x_0) &= \left(\frac{dF}{dx}\right)_{x_0} \\
&= \left[2gT_{c,x}(S_0 - S_{f,x})^3 x \frac{dT_{c,x}}{dx} - 3gT_{c,x}^2 x\left(S_0 - S_{f,x}\right)^2 \frac{dS_{f,x}}{dx} \right. \\
&\quad \left. + gT_{c,x}^2(S_0 - S_{f,x})^3 x \right]_{x_0}
\end{aligned}
$$

$$(8.40)$$

and so forth. This method has already been applied to very many situations encountered in this book. Since the efficacy of the method depends on an appropriate initial trial value x_0, it is recommended that the value, which corresponds to a gradient close to the specified gradient, should be taken as the initial trial value.

The geometric parameters in the expression $F(x)$ are taken as explicit functions of the critical depth, and their differential coefficients with respect to x are derived from the relationship

$$\frac{d}{dx} = \frac{dy_{c,x}}{dx}\frac{d}{dy_{c,x}}$$

In order to determine $dy_{c,x}/dx$, we proceed as follows:

The hydraulic depth at the critical section, located at a distance x from the upstream end of a channel, is given by the equation

$$D_{c,x} = \frac{U_{c,x}^2}{g} = \frac{Q_x^2}{A_{c,x}^2 g} = \frac{q_i^2 x^2}{A_{c,x}^2 g} \qquad (8.41)$$

where Q_x is the discharge at the critical section. Combining this equation with a similar equation for the critical hydraulic depth at the end of the channel $(x = L)$, we obtain

$$\frac{A_{c,x}^2 D_{c,x}}{A_{c,L}^2 D_{c,L}} = \left(\frac{x}{L}\right)^2$$

that is,

$$A_{c,x}^2 D_{c,x} = C_1 x^2 \qquad (8.42)$$

where

$$C_1 = \frac{A_{c,L}^2 D_{c,L}}{L^2} \qquad (8.43)$$

Hence, we obtain from Eq. (8.42) by differentiating

$$\left(2 A_{c,x} D_{c,x} \frac{dA_{c,x}}{dy_{c,x}} + A_{c,x}^2 \frac{dD_{c,x}}{dy_{c,x}}\right) \frac{dy_{c,x}}{dx} = 2 C_1 x$$

that is,

$$\frac{dy_{c,x}}{dx} = \frac{2 C_1 x}{2 A_{c,x} D_{c,x}(dA_{c,x}/dy_{c,x}) + A_{c,x}^2 (dD_{c,x}/dy_{c,x})}$$

$$= \frac{2 C_1 x}{2 A_{c,x} D_{c,x} T_{c,x} + A_{c,x}^2 (dD_{c,x}/dy_{c,x})} \qquad (8.44)$$

where

$$\frac{dD_{c,x}}{dy_{c,x}} = \frac{d}{dy_{c,x}}\left(\frac{A_{c,x}}{T_{c,x}}\right) = \frac{1}{T_{c,x}}\frac{dA_{c,x}}{dy_{c,x}} - \frac{A_{c,x}}{T_{c,x}^2}\frac{dT_{c,x}}{dy_{c,x}}$$

$$= 1 - \frac{A_{c,x}}{T_{c,x}^2}\frac{dT_{c,x}}{dy_{c,x}} \tag{8.45}$$

In special cases of triangular and rectangular channels, Eq. (8.44) assumes much simpler forms. These are derived as follows:

(a) *Triangular channel*

$$D_{c,x} = \frac{1}{2}y_{c,x}$$

$$T_{c,x} = (m_1 + m_2)y_{c,x}$$

$$A_{c,x} = \frac{1}{2}T_{c,x}y_{c,x} = \frac{1}{2}(m_1 + m_2)y_{c,x}^2$$

from Eq. (8.43), we obtain

$$C_1 = \frac{1}{8}(m_1 + m_2)^2\frac{y_{c,x}^5}{L^2}$$

When the corresponding values are substituted in Eq. (8.44), the result is

$$\frac{dy_{c,x}}{dx} = \frac{1/4(m_1 + m_2)^2 y_{c,L}^5(x/L^2)}{1/2(m_1 + m_2)^2 y_{c,x}^4 + 1/8(m_1 + m_2)^2 y_{c,x}^4} = \frac{2}{5}\frac{y_{c,L}^5}{y_{c,x}^4}\left(\frac{x}{L^2}\right)$$

which, in view of Eq. (8.17), reduces to

$$\frac{dy_{c,x}}{dx} = \frac{2}{5}\left(\frac{y_{c,L}}{L}\right)\left(\frac{L}{x}\right)^{-3/5} \tag{8.46}$$

This result could be obtained directly from Eq. (8.17).

(b) *Rectangular channel*

$$D_{c,x} = y_{c,x}$$

$$T_{c,x} = B$$

$$A_{c,x} = By_{c,x}$$

from Eq. (8.43), we obtain

$$C_1 = \frac{B^2 y_{c,x}^3}{L^2}$$

When the corresponding values are substituted in Eq. (8.44), the result is

$$\frac{dy_{c,x}}{dx} = \frac{2B^2 y_{c,L}^3 (x/L^2)}{3B^2 y_{c,x}^2} = \frac{2}{3} \frac{y_{c,L}^3}{y_{c,x}^2} \left(\frac{x}{L^2} \right)$$

which, in view of Eq. (8.21), reduces to

$$\frac{dy_{c,x}}{dx} = \frac{2}{3} \left(\frac{y_{c,L}}{L} \right) \left(\frac{L}{x} \right)^{-1/3} \tag{8.47}$$

This result could be obtained directly from Eq. (8.21).
From Eq. (8.10), the differential coefficient of $S_{f,x}$

$$\frac{dS_{f,x}}{dy_{c,x}} = n^2 g \left(\frac{1}{R_{c,x}^{4/3}} \frac{dD_{c,x}}{dy_{c,x}} - \frac{D_{c,x}}{R_{c,x}^{7/3}} \frac{dR_{c,x}}{dy_{c,x}} \right)$$

$$= S_{f,x} \left(\frac{1}{D_{c,x}} \frac{dD_{c,x}}{dy_{c,x}} - \frac{4}{3R_{c,x}} \frac{dR_{c,x}}{dy_{c,x}} \right) \tag{8.48}$$

where from the relationship

$$R = \frac{A}{P}$$

$$\frac{dR_{c,x}}{dy_{c,x}} = \frac{1}{P_{c,x}} \frac{dA_{c,x}}{dy_{c,x}} - \frac{A_{c,x}}{P_{c,x}^2} \frac{dP_{c,x}}{dy_{c,x}} = \frac{T_{c,x}}{P_{c,x}} - \frac{R_{c,x}}{P_{c,x}^2} \frac{dP_{c,x}}{dy_{c,x}} \tag{8.49}$$

From Eqs (8.40) and (8.49), we find that the geometric parameters required to be differentiated are only $T_{c,x}$ and $P_{c,x}$. This operation can be performed readily by using their expressions derived in section 2.4. We illustrate the procedure by considering the rectangular channel of Example 7.3 (Chapter 7) and Example 8.2.

Example 8.5: A rectangular channel 150 mm wide is laid at a uniform gradient of 2·5%. The channel carries rainwater discharge which increases linearly, and has a maximum value of 22·22 l/s. If the length of the channel is 50 m, locate the control section. Relocate the control section if the channel gradient increases to 4%.

Solution:

$$q_i = 22 \cdot 22/50 = 0 \cdot 4444 \, \text{l/s/m}$$

From Eq. (6.8)

$$y_{c,L} = \sqrt[3]{\frac{1}{9 \cdot 806} \left(\frac{0 \cdot 02222}{0 \cdot 15} \right)^2} = 0 \cdot 1308 \, \text{m}$$

$$A_{c,L} = 0 \cdot 15 \times 0 \cdot 1308 = 0 \cdot 01962 \, \text{m}^2$$
$$D_{c,L} = y_{c,L} = 0 \cdot 1308 \, \text{m}$$
$$P_{c,L} = B + 2y_{c,L} = 0 \cdot 15 + 0 \cdot 2616 = 0 \cdot 4116 \, \text{m}$$
$$R_{c,L} = 0 \cdot 01962/0 \cdot 4116 = 0 \cdot 04767 \, \text{m}$$

$$S_{f,L} = \frac{(0 \cdot 015^2)(9 \cdot 806)(0 \cdot 1308)}{0 \cdot 04767^{4/3}} = 0 \cdot 0167$$

From Eq. (8.14)

$$S_{0,L} = 0 \cdot 0167 + \frac{2 \times 0 \cdot 1308}{50 \cdot 0} = 0 \cdot 0219$$

since, $S_0 > S_{0,L}$, the control section is at $x < 50 \cdot 0 \, \text{m}$.

From Table 8.2, we find that, for $S_0 = 2 \cdot 5\%$, a suitable initial trial value of x is 3·0 m which corresponds to $S_{0,x} = 2 \cdot 45\%$. It takes two trials for the method, described in section 8.4, to converge to $x = 2 \cdot 715 \, \text{m}$. The accuracy of the method can be checked by verifying Eq. (8.8).

The computed value of the friction slope S_f at the control section is 1·118%. This value, and the specified channel gradient S_0 give the right-hand side of Eq. (8.8) as

$$\frac{8(0 \cdot 4444 \times 10^{-3})^2}{9 \cdot 806 \times 0 \cdot 0225 \times 0 \cdot 01382^3} = \frac{1 \cdot 58}{0 \cdot 5824} = 2 \cdot 713 \, \text{m}$$

which shows that the computed value of x is accurate within 2 mm.

By inspection of values in Table 8.2, the control section for $S_0 = 4\cdot0\%$ is at $0\cdot4$ m from the upstream end. The friction slope at the assumed control section is $1\cdot39\%$. These values give the right-hand side of Eq. (8.8) as

$$\frac{8(0\cdot4444 \times 10^{-3})^2}{9\cdot806 \times 0\cdot0225 \times 0\cdot0261^3} = \frac{1\cdot58}{3\cdot9228} = 0\cdot403 \text{ m}$$

which shows that the computed value of x is accurate within 3 mm.

9

Design of channels carrying linearly varied flow I: spacing of outlets

This chapter focuses on the calculation of outlet spacing required in the design of a drainage scheme. For the conventional system of drainage, the method is based on recommendations from the Highway Agency, while, for a linear drainage system, the varied flow theory forms the method basis. It is found that the computation of the flow profile is significantly important in the design of the outlet spacing for linear drainage systems.

9.1 Highway drainage systems

The traditional and still widely used method of disposal of surplus rainwater from road surfaces is by means of open channels carrying water parallel to the kerb. It is common to construct a triangular channel, with the kerb face as its vertical side and a limited width of the carriageway, with a certain amount of cross fall, as the sloping side (Fig. 1.1). Other shapes, such as rectangular and trapezoidal, are less common. The allowable width of flow, denoted by W_f, depends on the type of road construction. For instance, in trunk roads it should not exceed $1.5\,\text{m}$ if there is a hard shoulder, and $1.0\,\text{m}$ if there is a hard strip. For shopping precincts its value is limited to $0.5\,\text{m}$. In order to keep the width of water within these limits, the flow in the channel has to be intercepted at appropriate points by means of gullies with grated tops, or by openings in the kerb, called kerb inlets. The water that runs through these accessories is discharged into a receiving channel that may be a natural watercourse or a storm sewer or, alternatively, the water may be discharged directly into fields for irrigation.

Linear drainage channels, introduced in Chapter 1, are often combined with kerbs. The depth of flow in these channels is restricted by their internal height, requiring the flow to leave the channel at suitably located outfalls. An outfall is usually made from one of the units by opening an aperture at the bottom. The capacity of a linear drainage system is defined by the rate of discharge at the outlet when the depth of flow anywhere in the channel reaches the permissible value.

The spacing between gullies or kerb inlets of the traditional drainage system, or the channel length between two adjacent outfalls of a linear drainage system, are important design features of a drainage scheme. An adequate outlet spacing ensures that the flow-carrying capacity of the system does not fall below the rate of the flow entering the channel. The general practice adopted in the design of the spacing is to consider the segment of the channel between two adjacent outlets as an independent channel.

Theoretically, the outlet spacing depends on the capacity of the channel which, in turn, depends on the longitudinal gradient, the geometry of the cross section of the channel and the roughness of the channel surface. This is true for both modes of water disposal. However, the procedure recommended by *Advisory Note HA102* [9.1], assumes that the limiting factor in determining the spacing of gullies and kerb inlets is the capacity of the grating. There are also other factors that often decide the location of the outlets. These are

(a) The maintenance of the gullies does not cause any restriction to the traffic.

(b) There must be a gully, or preferably two, at a sag point in case there is one. This is because, due to floating debris, the collecting efficiency of the gully at a sag point is substantially low.

(c) Although, no gully is normally required at a well defined crest, if there is a slow transition from a negative to a positive gradient, that is, there is a flat gradient for a significant distance, then a gully may be needed at the crest.

Let us begin with the derivation of the channel length by the method recommended by HA102/00, and we will follow it by applying the varied flow theory discussed in Chapters 7 and 8.

9.2 Spacing of gullies and kerb inlets from HA102

According to the method discussed in reference [9.1], the computation starts with an assumed time of concentration T, and ends with verifying it with the calculated value. As in the Lloyd-Davies formula (section 1.3.1), the time of concentration is defined by the sum

$$T = T_s + T_g \tag{9.1}$$

where T_s = time taken by water to flow from the farthest point on the road surface to the kerb, and T_g = time of flow along the kerb.

The basis of the initial estimate of T is that, if the spacing between gullies is to be less than $10\,m$, then $T < 5$ minutes and, if the spacing between gullies is to be greater than $50\,m$ then $T > 5$ minutes. From this point, the procedure is as follows:

Step 1
Apply the assumed time of concentration to calculate the design intensity of rainfall I from the formula

$$I = \frac{32.7(N - 0.4)^{0.223}(T - 0.4)^{0.565}(M_{5-2\,\text{min}})}{T} \tag{9.2}$$

where N = storm return period in years, T = time of concentration in minutes, and $M_{5-2\,\text{min}}$ = depth of rainfall of 2 minute duration and 5 year return period.

The value of $M_{5-2\,\text{min}}$, for the use in Great Britain and Northern Ireland, is obtained from Fig. 9.1.

Step 2
Determine the capacity of the proposed channel from the equation of the uniform flow theory, that is,

$$Q = AU \tag{9.3}$$

where

$$U = \frac{R^{2/3} S_0^{1/2}}{n} \tag{9.4}$$

and A is the cross-sectional area of the flow.

In order to accommodate any variability of the longitudinal gradient, the value of S_0 is taken as the estimated average over a distance of $3\,m$ upstream of the gully. Likewise, the cross fall, S_c required in determining the hydraulic parameters of the channel, is measured $0.5\,m$ upstream of the leading edge of the gully. The cross-sectional area of flow is based on the maximum permissible width of the flow. The value of Q thus determined must *not exceed* the capacity of the gully pot, which may have the following values:

$10\,l/s$ for a $100\,mm$ diameter pipe
$15\,l/s$ for a $150\,mm$ diameter pipe

Step 3
Determine the area A_d, the drainage system is capable of handling, from the equation

$$A_d = \frac{3600Q}{I} \tag{9.5}$$

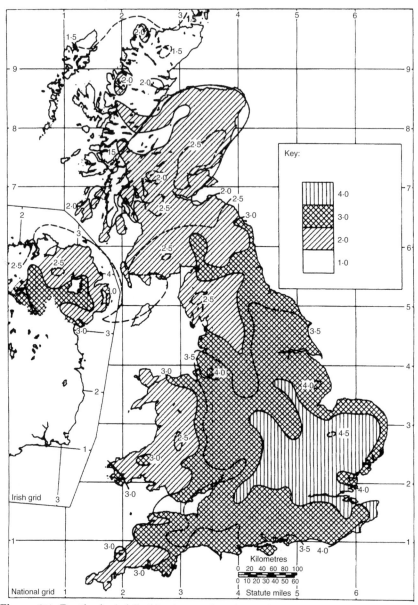

Figure 9.1 *Depth of rainfall of 2 minutes duration and 5 year return period (Great Britain and Ireland).*

Step 4

Determine the actual area A_a drained. According to the method discussed in reference [9.1], the actual area drained (A_a) is related to the area required to be drained (A_d) through the equation

$$A_a = (m)(\eta)A_d \tag{9.6}$$

where m = maintenance factor for the gully, and η = flow collection efficiency of the gully, or that of the kerb inlet.

The maintenance factor varies from 0·7 at sag points, to 1·0 for well maintained urban roads, and the efficiency of the gully is derived from the grating parameter G defined by the equation

$$G = \frac{69}{A_g} \frac{C_b}{\sqrt{p}} \tag{9.7}$$

In this equation, A_g = grating area in mm², which is the area of the smallest rectangle parallel to the kerb that just includes all the bars, p = waterway area expressed as a percentage of the grating area, $C_b = 1·75$ for transverse bars, and $C_b = 1·5$ for other bar alignment.

Depending on the value of G, measured in seconds/m², and calculated from Eq. (9.7), gratings are divided into various types, each identified by a label, and assigned with a design value G_d of the grating parameter. The labels are in alphabetical order, ranging from P for which $G_d = 30\,\text{s/m}^2$, to T *for which* $G_d = 110\,\text{s/m}^2$ (see Table B2 of reference [9.1]).

The efficiency of the gully, expressed as percentage, is calculated from the equation

$$\eta = 100 - G_d \frac{Q}{h} \tag{9.8}$$

where Q is the maximum discharge carried by the channel, and h is the design depth of water in the channel.

The efficiency of the kerb inlet, also expressed as percentage, is calculated from the equation

$$\eta = 100 - \frac{36 \cdot 1 Q}{L_i h^{1 \cdot 5}} \tag{9.9}$$

where L_i is the length (in metres) of the opening in the line of the kerb. The discharge Q is calculated just upstream of the gully.

Step 5
Determine the gully spacing L from the equation

$$L = \frac{A_a}{W_e} \qquad (9.10)$$

where W_e is the effective width of the catchment area.

Step 6
Determine the time of flow in the channel from the equation

$$T_g = \frac{L}{U} \qquad (9.11)$$

Step 7
Calculate the time of concentration by adding T_g to T_s.
    The design is satisfactory when the time of concentration obtained at the end of Step 7 agrees with the assumed value T.

Example 9.1: A road is constructed at a uniform longitudinal gradient of 1:150, and a cross fall of 1:40. The design return period is 5 years, and the grating to be used is of the type R for which $G_a = 60{\cdot}0\,\text{s/m}^2$. Using the following data, determine the gully spacing.

$$W_f = 1{\cdot}0\,\text{m}$$
$$M_{5\text{-}2\,\text{min}} = 4\,\text{mm}$$
$$m = 0{\cdot}9$$
$$W_e = 10{\cdot}45\,\text{m}$$
$$n = 0{\cdot}017$$

Capacity of gully pot $= 10\,\text{l/s}$

Solution: Assuming $T = 4{\cdot}0$ minutes, we obtain from Eq. (9.2)

$$I = \frac{32{\cdot}7(4{\cdot}6)^{0{\cdot}223}(3{\cdot}6)^{0{\cdot}565}(4{\cdot}0)}{4{\cdot}0} = 94{\cdot}8\,\text{mm/hr}$$

The allowable depth of flow h is given by

$$h = W_f\,S_c = 0{\cdot}025\,\text{m}$$

To determine the discharge, we first determine

$$A = \frac{1}{2}hW_f = \frac{1}{2}0{\cdot}025 \times 1{\cdot}0 = 0{\cdot}0125\,\text{m}^2$$

$$P = h + \sqrt{W_f^2 + h^2} = 0{\cdot}025 + 1{\cdot}0003 = 1{\cdot}0253\,\text{m}$$

$$R = \frac{A}{P} = 0.01219 \text{ m} \qquad R^{2/3} = 0.05297$$

From Eq. (9.4)

$$U = \frac{0.05297\sqrt{1/150}}{0.017} = 0.2544 \text{ m/s}$$

and, from Eq. (9.3),

$$Q = 0.0125 \times 0.2544 \times 1000 = 3.2 \text{ l/s}$$

This value, being considerably less than the capacity of the gully pot (10 l/s minimum), is allowed.

From Eq. (9.5)

$$A_d = \frac{3600 \times 3.2}{94.8} = 121.5 \text{ m}^2$$

From Eq. (9.8)

$$\eta = 100 - 60\frac{3.2 \times 10^{-3}}{0.025} = 93\%$$

From Eq. (9.6)

$$A_a = (0.9)(0.93)(121.5) = 101.7 \text{ m}^2$$

From Eq. (9.10)

$$L = \frac{101.7}{10.45} = 9.7 \text{ m}$$

Check for time of concentration
From Eq. (9.11)

$$T_g = \frac{L}{U} = \frac{9.7}{(0.2544 \times 60)} = 0.64 \text{ minute}$$

Assuming $T_s = 3$ minutes, we obtain from $T = 3.64$ minutes, which, when rounded off to 4 minutes, equals the assumed time of concentration.

If there is a crest in the road surface, it is usual to start the computations with finding the distance from the crest to the nearest gully. *The slope used in calculating this distance is the estimated longitudinal slope of the channel 3 m upstream of the gully.* The following example illustrates the working of the method in such a situation.

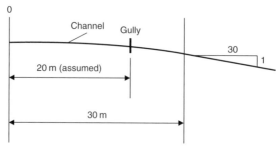

Figure 9.2 *Spacing of gullies (Example 9.1).*

Example 9.2: The longitudinal gradient of a road varies from zero at the crest to 1:30 at 30 m from the crest, and is uniform thereafter (see Fig. 9.2). Using the data of Example 9.1, determine the gully spacing.

Solution: Assuming that the gully next to the crest is 20 m downstream of it, the estimated longitudinal gradient at 3 m upstream of the gully = 1/50. This gives the velocity of flow in the channel

$$U = \frac{0 \cdot 05297 \sqrt{1/50}}{0 \cdot 017} = 0 \cdot 441 \text{ m/s}$$

The channel capacity $Q = 0 \cdot 0125 \times 0 \cdot 441 \times 1000 = 5 \cdot 5$ l/s

Again, the capacity discharge is sufficiently less than the capacity of the gully pot.

From Eq. (9.8)

$$\eta = 100 - 60 \frac{5 \cdot 5 \times 10^{-3}}{0 \cdot 025} = 87\%$$

From Eq. (9.6)

$$A_a = (0 \cdot 9)(0 \cdot 87) \frac{5 \cdot 5 \times 3600}{94 \cdot 8} = 178 \cdot 2 \text{ m}^2$$

From Eq. (9.10)

$$L = \frac{178 \cdot 2}{10 \cdot 45} = 17 \cdot 0 \text{ m}$$

which, when compared with the assumed length of 20 m, is about right.
The actual time of concentration is given by

$$T = 3 \cdot 0 + \frac{17 \cdot 0}{0 \cdot 441 \times 60} = 3 \cdot 64 \text{ minutes.}$$

This value, when rounded off to 4 minutes, agrees with the assumed value of T.

The spacing of the downstream gullies is determined for $S_0 = 1/30$, at which

$$U = \frac{0 \cdot 05297 \sqrt{1/30}}{0 \cdot 017} = 0 \cdot 569 \text{ m/s}$$

giving

$$Q = 0 \cdot 0125 \times 0 \cdot 569 \times 1000 = 7 \cdot 1 \, l/s$$

From Eq. (9.8)

$$\eta = 100 - 60 \frac{7 \cdot 1 \times 10^{-3}}{0 \cdot 025} = 83 \cdot 0\%$$

From Eq. (9.5)

$$A_d = \frac{7 \cdot 1 \times 3600}{94 \cdot 8} = 270 \cdot 0 \text{ m}^2$$

From Eq. (9.6)

$$A_a = (0 \cdot 9)(0 \cdot 83)(270) = 201 \cdot 4 \, \text{m}^2$$

From Eq. (9.10)

$$L = \frac{201 \cdot 4}{10 \cdot 45} = 19 \cdot 3 \text{ m}$$

hence, we obtain

$$T_g = \frac{L}{U} = \frac{19 \cdot 3}{(0 \cdot 569 \times 60)} = 0 \cdot 57 \text{ minute}$$

which gives

$$T = 3 \cdot 57 \text{ minutes}$$

9.2.1 Maximum design spacing of gullies

The *maximum allowable spacing* for intermediate gullies may be calculated from the equations

$$L = \frac{3 \cdot 6 \times 10^6 Q(m\eta/100)}{W_e I} \tag{9.12}$$

for uniform longitudinal gradient

and

$$L = \frac{3\cdot6 \times 10^6 \left[Q - Q_{us}\left(1 - (m_{us}\eta_{us}/100)\right)\right]}{W_e I} \tag{9.13}$$

for non-uniform longitudinal gradient.

The quantities Q_{us}, m_{us} and η_{us} in Eq. (9.13) refer to the upstream gully. Calculations using this equation should start from the upstream end. If the upstream end is at the top of a crest where there is no gully, Q_{us} becomes zero.

Corresponding to the example just considered, we have

$$L = \frac{3\cdot6 \times 10^6 \times 7\cdot1 \times 10^{-3} \times 0\cdot9 \times 0\cdot83}{10\cdot45 \times 94\cdot8} = 19\cdot3 \text{ m}$$

9.3 Determination of channel lengths from varied flow theory

In a real situation, the amount of flow in the surface drainage channel increases while the channel dimensions remain constant. In applying the varied flow theory, the increase in the volume of flow is assumed to be linear, and is translated into a variation of the depth of flow shown by the flow profile. Derived from this, the criterion for the design of a drainage channel, is that the *maximum depth of flow, anywhere in the channel, should not exceed the prescribed limit.* The step method of computation of the flow profile in a channel, which leads to the determination of the maximum depth and its location, has been described in Chapters 7 and 8. Here, the method is applied to the design of the outlet spacing for a channel intercepted by a series of outlets. Let us begin by finding the outlet spacing in a horizontal channel, although such a channel is of more common occurrence in roof guttering than in highway drainage systems.

9.3.1 Horizontal channel

In a horizontal channel, the depth of flow is maximum at the cross section O, midway between the outlets A and B (see Fig. 9.3). The flow profile is symmetrical about O, across which there is no flow. Hence, the channel AB can be divided into two independent segments, one with its downstream end at A, and the other with its downstream end at B, with the upstream

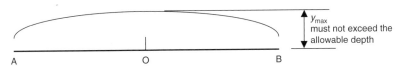

Figure 9.3 *Flow profile of a horizontal drainage channel with outlets at A and B.*

ends of both segments being at O. To this configuration, we apply the following procedure for the calculation of the spacing L:

1. From the given rate of inflow q_i, determine the rate of flow, say, at the outlet B from the equation

$$Q_B = \frac{1}{2} q_i L \tag{9.12}$$

2. Starting at B, solve the varied flow equation, and determine the depth of flow at O.
3. Adjust the length according to the depth of flow at O being greater, or less, than the specified depth of the system.

If, instead of starting at B, the computation starts at A, the result will be the same, for the rate of flow Q_A at A is the same as Q_B.

Let us now consider the channel in Example 9.1 laid horizontally. The rate of inflow due to a rainfall of 94·8 mm/hr, over a 10·45 m wide pavement is given by

$$q_i = \frac{94·8 \times 10·45}{3600} = 0·275 \text{ l/s/m}$$

Assuming an initial gully spacing of 12 m, the step method gives the depth of flow midway between the two adjacent gullies as 27·12 mm. Since this is greater than the allowable depth of 25 mm, the spacing has to be reduced. A spacing of 10·0 m, which gives the maximum depth of flow of 25·0 mm, is accepted. The area drained is given by

$$A_d = 10·0 \times 10·45 = 104·5 \text{ m}^2$$

Discharge from the drained area

$$Q = \frac{104·5 \times 94·8}{3600} = 2·75 \text{ l/s}$$

From Eq. (9.8)

$$\eta = 100 - 60 \frac{2·75 \times 10^{-3}}{0·025} = 93·4\%$$

Table 9.1 *Velocity profile for channel of Example 9.1 (see Fig. 9.3)*

Distance from upstream outlet (m)	Velocity (m/s)
0	0·0
0·5	0·0103
1·0	0·0206
1·5	0·0311
2·0	0·0420
2·5	0·0534
3·0	0·0657
3·5	0·0795
4·0	0·0960
4·5	0·1178
5·0	0·2778

At this value of the collecting efficiency of the gully, and allowing for the maintenance factor of 0·9, the actual area drained is given by

$$A_a = 0·934 \times 0·9 \times 104·5 = 87·84 \, m^2$$

Hence, the gully spacing L is to be modified to

$$L = \frac{87·84}{104·5} \times 10·0 = 8·4 \, m.$$

The time taken for water to flow in the channel, from the first point of entry to the outlet is calculated on the basis of the average velocity of flow. For instance, the velocities in the channel considered in this example are given in Table. 9.1 (see also Fig. 9.4). Using the trapezoidal rule, the average velocity of flow U is calculated as 0·0655 m/s. Hence, from Eqs (9.1) and (9.11)

$$T = 3·0 + \frac{4·2}{0·0655 \times 60} = 4·07 \text{ minutes}$$

which verifies the assumed time of concentration.

9.3.2   Channel laid at a gradient

By introducing a gradient to a channel, however small, the location of the maximum depth moves downstream (see Fig. 9.5). As a consequence, the depth of flow falls upstream of O, and rises downstream of O, which means that there is no point of symmetry for the flow profile, and the water flows

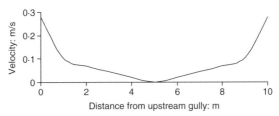

Figure 9.4 *Variation of velocity of flow in a horizontal channel between adjacent gullies.*

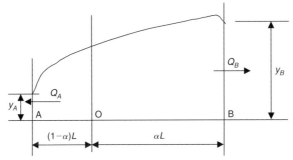

Figure 9.5 *Flow profile of an inclined horizontal drainage channel with outlets at both ends.*

through the outlets B and A at unequal rates. These are given by the equations

$$Q_B = \alpha q_i L \tag{9.13}$$

$$Q_A = (1 - \alpha)q_i L \tag{9.14}$$

where α is the fraction of the total length L contributing to the flow through the outlet B. The contribution to the flow through the outlet A is from the length $(1 - \alpha)L$. The situation requires independent treatment of the two newly created segments of the channel, one of length αL, and the other of $(1 - \alpha)L$. In order to compute the flow profile for the channel AB, it is necessary to satisfy the requirement that the depth of flow at $x = \alpha L$, where x is measured from A, calculated for both sections has the same value. This is an additional condition to be imposed on the solution when extending the procedure for a horizontal channel in order to apply it to a channel laid at a gradient. However, because of the numerical nature of the solution, it is not possible to determine α precisely, and an acceptable level of tolerance has to be allowed. This problem is overcome by using a fast digital computer, and it is possible to adjust both α and L, so that the difference in the depth of flow at O obtained from the two solutions is small, say less than one millimetre, and the length of the channel is determined with a fairly high level of accuracy.

It can be seen that, for a horizontal channel α is 0·5, and its magnitude increases with the gradient. In the limiting case when the entire flow passes through B, $\alpha = 1·0$, which means that the outlet A becomes redundant as far as the channel AB is concerned.

Let us now apply this method to determine the gully spacing of Example 9.1. Starting with an initial length of 10 m, and a value of $\alpha = 0·8$, the solution for $S_0 = 1/150$ converges to the following values:

$$L = 10·2\,\text{m}$$

$$\alpha = 0·978$$

The two segments of the channel, which contribute to the flow through the two gullies A and B, are shown in Fig. 9.6. These segments meet at O which is at 0·22 m from the upstream gully. The computed depths of flow at O is 7·91 mm from segment AO, and 7·94 mm from segment BO, which shows a discrepancy of only 0·03 mm.

Assuming that the gullies are spaced at equal distances, we find from the value of α that the total flow through each gully is made up of 97·8% of the flow in the channel upstream and 2·2% from the channel downstream of it.

The area drained is given by

$$A_d = 10·2 \times 10·45 = 106·6\,\text{m}^2$$

Discharge from the drained area is given by

$$Q = \frac{106·6 \times 94·8}{3600} = 2·80\,\text{l/s}$$

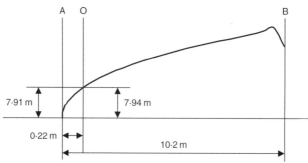

Figure 9.6 *Flow profile between gullies A and B.*

From Eq. (9.8)

$$\eta = 100 - 60\frac{2\cdot8 \times 10^{-3}}{0\cdot025} = 93\cdot3\%$$

At this value of the collecting efficiency of the gully, and allowing for the maintenance factor of $0\cdot9$, the actual area drained is given by

$$A_a = 0\cdot933 \times 0\cdot9 \times 106\cdot6 = 89\cdot5\,\text{m}^2$$

Hence, the gully spacing L is modified to

$$L = 10\cdot2 \times \frac{89\cdot5}{106\cdot6} = 8\cdot6\,\text{m}$$

In order to further the understanding of channels with two outlets, let us consider the following example of a rectangular channel dealt with in reference [7.1].

Example 9.3: A rectangular channel 150 mm wide has outlets at both ends. The channel carries rainwater discharge from a 40 m wide pavement over which the intensity of rainfall is 40 mm/hr. If the length of the channel is 50 m, compute the flow profiles for the channel gradients 0·0%, 1·0% and 2·0%. Manning's n is 0·015.

Solution: Assuming the runoff coefficient as 1·0, the rate of inflow is given by

$$q_i = \frac{40\cdot0 \times 40\cdot0}{3600} = 0\cdot4444\,\text{l/s/m}$$

Following the procedure outlined above, the varied flow equation can be solved. The solution starts at A and B, separately, and considering each specified gradient in turn. For the horizontal channel, $\alpha = 0\cdot5$. As the gradient increases, higher values of α are assumed. These values are adjusted until the depth at $x = (1 - \alpha)L$, obtained from the two solutions, are reasonably close.

The adjusted values of α and the depths of flow along the channel length, are given in Table 9.2. The Froude numbers, also given in the table, indicate that (a) both ends of the channel are control sections, and (b) as the gradient increases, the velocity of flow increases and becomes critical in the entire channel when the gradient is about 2·0% The flow profiles are given in Fig. 9.7.

Table 9.2 *Flow profiles for a rectangular channel with outlets at both ends (Example 9.3)*

x (m)	$S_0 = 0$ $\alpha = 0 \cdot 5$		$S_0 = 1/500$ $\alpha = 0 \cdot 666$		$S_0 = 1/200$ $\alpha = 0 \cdot 8708$		$S_0 = 1/100$ $\alpha = 0 \cdot 9883$		$S_0 = 1/50$ $\alpha = 0 \cdot 998852$	
	y	F	y	F	y	F	y	F	y	F
0	82·4	1·00	63·0	1·00	33·4	1·00	6·7	1·00	1·4	1·00
5	142·8	0·35	121·5	0·26	85·7	0·053	45·6	0·43	29·6	0·92
10	158·3	0·23	140·0	0·12	110·0	0·10	67·6	0·51	45·3	0·98
15	165·9	0·14	152·3	0·026	130·0	0·17	87·0	0·53	58·7	0·99
20	169·4	0·068	162·0	0·048	147·0	0·23	105·0	0·54	71·0	0·99
25	170·3	0·0	169·7	0·11	161·0	0·27	121·8	0·54	82·7	0·99
30	169·4	0·068	175·0	0·17	172·2	0·31	137·2	0·55	94·0	0·98
35	165·4	0·14	175·8	0·23	180·3	0·35	151·1	0·55	105·0	0·97
40	158·3	0·23	172·2	0·33	181·0	0·41	162·0	0·57	115·7	0·96
45	142·8	0·35	160·0	0·45	175·0	0·50	166·9	0·62	126·3	0·95
50	82·4	1·0	99·8	1·0	119·3	1·0	129·8	1·0	130·7	1·0

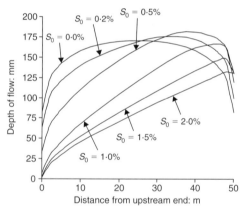

Figure 9.7 *Flow profiles for a rectangular channel with outlets at both ends (Example 9.3).*

Table 9.3 contains maximum depths of flow in the channel of Example 9.3, with one or two outlets. By comparing the two sets of values, the following conclusions can be drawn:

(*a*) While the maximum depth of flow in the channel with single outlet decreases as the gradient increases, the maximum depth in a channel with two outlets rises as the gradient increases from zero to about 0·5% (Fig. 9.8). After this, the maximum depth decreases. A greater depth of flow requires shorter length of the channel. When the

Table 9.3 *Maximum depth of flow (y) and its location (x) in a rectangular channel with one or two outlets (Example 9.3)*

Gradient	Maximum depth y (mm) and distance x (m) from the upstream end			
	One outlet		Two outlets	
	y	x	y	x
0	290·8	0·0	170·3	25·0
1/500	239·3	27·0	174·9	30·7
1/200	201·7	38·0	181·7	39·5
1/100	168·3	45·0	166·9	44·5
1/50	136·2	49·5	136·1	49·5
1/25	100·0	50·0		
1/10	100·0	50·0		

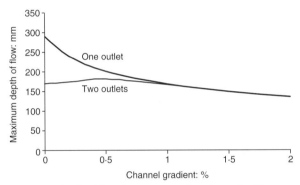

Figure 9.8 *Maximum depth of flow in a rectangular channel with one or two outlets (Example 9.3).*

gradient is about 2·0%, the two flow profiles become identical, attaining the same maximum depth.

(b) In terms of the maximum depths of flow, the effectiveness of a horizontal channel with outlets at both ends, and that of a channel laid at a gradient of 1·0% are nearly the same (see also reference [7.1]).

Similar conclusions can be drawn for channels of other shapes. Let us, for instance, consider a triangular channel and a trapezoidal channel of the same length, and carrying the same volume of water, as in the above example of a rectangular channel. Let the dimensions of these channels be as follows:

Triangular channel $m_1 = 0$ $m_2 = 1/20$
Trapezoidal channel $m_1 = 1·0$ $m_2 = 1/5$ $B = 0·203\,\text{m}$

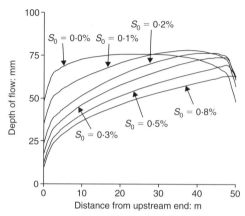

Figure 9.9 *Flow profiles for a triangular channel with outlets at both ends.*

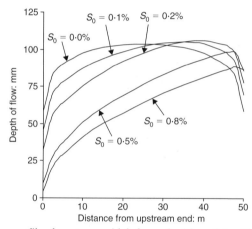

Figure 9.10 *Flow profiles for a trapezoidal channel with outlets at both ends.*

The corresponding flow profiles (see Figs 9.9 and 9.10) show similar characteristic features as in Fig. 9.7. See also Tables 9.4 and 9.5.

As a final example, reconsider the triangular channel of Example 9.2, and calculate the channel lengths (gully spacings) for longitudinal gradients of 1/50 and 1/30 using the varied flow theory. At these gradients, the entire flow in the channel between two adjacent gullies is discharged into the downstream gully, the following is the outcome of the analysis:

Channel at

$$S_0 = \frac{1}{50}$$

Table 9.4 *Maximum depths and locations in a triangular channel with outlets at both ends*

| Gradient | Maximum depth y (mm) and distance x (m) from the upstream end | | | | |
| | One outlet | | Two outlets | | |
	y	x	α	y	x
0	103·1	0·0	0·5	75·7	25·0
1/1000	86·3	36·0	0·7769	78·1	38·5
1/500	79·4	42·0	0·91695	76·8	42·4
1/200	69·5	48·5	0·98508	69·1	48·0
1/125	64·6	49·5	0·993734	64·5	49·5
1/100	61·4	50·0			
1/50	53·7	50·0			
1/20	45·0	50·0			
1/10	39·3	50·0			

Table 9.5 *Maximum depth of flow and its location in a trapezoidal channel with one or two outlets*

| Gradient | Maximum depth y (mm) and distance x (m) from the upstream end | | | | |
| | One outlet | | Two outlets | | |
	y	x	α	y	x
0	153·6	0·0	0·5	103·5	25·0
1/1000	130·0	36·0	0·6728	105·5	34·8
1/500	118·3	42·0	0·8139	106·4	39·4
1/200	100·2	47·0	0·971	98·7	47·1
1/125	91·0	49·0	0·9915	90·6	49·0
1/100	84·7	50·0			
1/50	68·5	50·0			
1/20	52·2	50·0			
1/10	42·6	50·0			

The control section occurs at 3 m from the upstream gully.

Limiting the maximum depth of flow to 25 mm, the length of the channel is found to be 19·2 m. From the estimated average velocity of flow of 0·38 m/s,

Time of flow

$$T_g = \frac{L}{U} = \frac{19\cdot2}{(0\cdot38 \times 60)} = 0\cdot84 \text{ minute}$$

Channel at

$$S_0 = \frac{1}{30}$$

The control section occurs at the upstream gully. Again, limiting the maximum depth of flow to 25 mm, the length of the channel is found to be 25·2 m, and the estimated average velocity of flow to be 0·47 m/s. From this, we determine

Time of flow

$$T_g = \frac{L}{U} = \frac{25\cdot2}{(0\cdot47 \times 60)} = 0\cdot89 \text{ minute}$$

The corresponding time of concentration for both channels is approximated to 4·0 minutes.

Reference

[9.1] *Design Manual for Roads and Bridges*, Vol. 4, Section 2, Drainage, Part 3 (HA 102/00) 2000.

10

Design of channels carrying linearly varied flow II: capacity of linear drainage systems

Beginning with a brief account of empirical methods of calculating the flow carrying capacity of a channel, this chapter focuses on the calculation of capacities of drainage channels. Both roof gutters and highway drainage channels are considered. The method follows directly from the computation of channel lengths discussed in Chapter 9.

10.1 Capacity of a linear drainage channel using empirical formulae

One of the earliest attempts to determine the capacity of roof gutters of various shapes is due to Beij [10.1]. Assuming the flow to be without friction, and using a dimensional analysis, Beij developed the following formulae for the capacities of horizontal channels:

(*a*) Semicircular gutter

$$Q = \sqrt{\frac{gd^5}{118 \cdot 592}} \tag{10.1}$$

where d = diameter of gutter

(*b*) Rectangular gutter

$$Q = 1 \cdot 3657 \left(\frac{h}{B}\right)^{8/5} \left(\frac{B}{L}\right)^{3/10} \sqrt{gB^5} \tag{10.2}$$

where h = depth of the gutter, B = width of the gutter, and L = length of the gutter.

Recently, Escarameia *et al.* [10.2] published the following empirical formula for calculating the capacity of drainage channels:

$$Q = 2\cdot66 A^{1.25}\left(6\cdot74 S_0^{0.7} + 0\cdot4 + \frac{L}{h}b\right) \tag{10.3}$$

where

for $S_0 \leqslant 1/200$ $b = 0\cdot132 S_0 - 0\cdot00022$

for $1/200 < S_0 \leqslant 1/30$ $b = 0\cdot00044$

and h is the design water depth. This formula was the outcome of an experimental investigation carried out at the Hydraulic Research Station, Wallingford, which involved various standards of linear drainage channels.

Example 10.1: Determine the capacity of a horizontally laid linear drainage channel of equivalent rectangular cross section of Example 7.9:

$$B = 237\,\text{mm} \qquad h = 335\,\text{mm}$$

Solution: Substitution of these values in Eq. (10.2) gives

$$Q = 1\cdot3657\left(\frac{0\cdot355}{0\cdot237}\right)^{8/5}\left(\frac{0\cdot237}{25\cdot0}\right)^{3/10}\sqrt{9\cdot806 \times (0\cdot237)^5}$$

$$= 1\cdot3657 \times 1\cdot9088 \times 0\cdot2472 \times 0\cdot08563$$

$$= 0\cdot055\,\text{m}^3/\text{s} = 55\cdot0\,\text{l/s}$$

Assuming the length of the channel $L = 20\,\text{m}$, we have

$$\frac{L}{h} = \frac{20\cdot0}{0\cdot335} = 59\cdot70$$

$$b = -0\cdot00022$$

$$A = 0\cdot237 \times 0\cdot335 = 0\cdot079\,\text{m}^2$$

These values, when substituted in Eq. (10.3), give

$$Q = 2\cdot66 \times 0\cdot042 \times (0\cdot4 - 59\cdot7 \times 0\cdot00022) = 0\cdot043\,\text{m}^3/\text{s} = 43\cdot0\,\text{l/s}$$

10.2   Capacity of a linear drainage channel from the variable flow theory

In Chapter 9, the theory of varied flow in determining the length of a linear drainage system was applied. For a given rate of inflow, the flow profile gave the depth of flow in the entire channel, and the criterion of the maximum depth of flow not exceeding the available internal height of the system gave the maximum allowable length of the channel. The capacity of the channel follows immediately after this calculation, for it is the rate of discharge at the outlet of the channel of maximum length. This shows that the capacity of a linear drainage system is dependent on the length of the channel, an argument supported by the fact that the surface friction varies along the length of the channel and, hence, the length of the channel must influence its capacity. However, it will be seen that, unless the channel is laid nearly level, the dependence of the capacity upon the length of the channel is limited to a relatively short distance from the outlet. In the case of a channel that is nearly level, the capacity of the channel decreases very slowly as the distance from the outlet increases, and attains the value given by the uniform flow theory (see reference [10.3]). This is evident in Fig. 10.4, which shows the capacities of a circular pipe laid at various gradients.

Consider the equation for the discharge Q at the outlet of a channel of length L:

$$Q = q_i L \qquad\qquad (10.4)$$

where q_i an arbitrary rate of inflow. It can be seen from this equation that if, for a specified value of q_i, L is the maximum allowable length of the channel, then Q is the capacity of the channel. If, however, the length of the channel is specified, and the capacity of the channel is required, then one can adjust q_i so that the criterion applied in the determination of the maximum length of the channel, is satisfied. From the adjusted value of q_i, the capacity of the channel is obtained directly from Eq. (10.4).

In order to understand the performance of a drainage system, it is usual to require the capacity of a channel for various length and slope combinations, and the calculations must be repeated each time the maximum depth anywhere in the channel is checked against the available internal height of the system.

In this chapter, this line is followed to determine the capacities of roof gutters and of channels used in highway construction. The method of computation is based on the step method discussed in earlier chapters and, for the sake of expediency, the step size is taken as $L/10$ throughout. It is found that, by reducing the step size, the computed capacity assumes a higher value, from which it is concluded that the values given here are somewhat on the conservative side.

10.3 Roof gutters

Recommendations regarding the use of various materials, and the factors that govern the design of roof gutters are detailed in BS 6367 [10.4].

The component of a roof drainage system, which is the main subject matter for the design, is the gutter or the channel that collects water from the almost impervious roof of the building, and the focus of design is the capacity of the channel to ensure its capability to handle the discharge. Other components of the system, namely, the outlets from the gutter itself, and the pipework that conveys the flow from the outlets to the below-ground system are made sufficiently large for a free discharge of flow from the gutter. These are not considered here. Since a roof gutter is nominally level (the slope being not steeper than 1:350), its capacity is dependent only on the size and shape of the cross section, the surface friction is considered only when the length of the gutter exceeds 50 times its overall depth.

A roof gutter may either be an eaves gutter provided along the edge of the roof, or a valley, parapet or boundary-wall gutter provided according to the need. The cross section of an *eaves gutter* is usually semicircular, and its capacity is calculated on the basis of the channel just flowing full, with no allowance made for freeboard. Capacities of eaves gutters of standard sizes ranging from 75 mm to 150 mm are given in Table 1 of reference [10.4]. These values are subject to reduction factors if

(a) the length of the gutter is more than 50 times the overall depth of the gutter,
(b) there is a bend in the channel, or
(c) if the gutter includes an angle.

The shape of a *valley, parapet* or *boundary-wall gutter* should conform to that of the cross section of the roof. However, for design purpose, a trapezoidal, rectangular or triangular shape is considered. The recommendations, regarding the dimensions of these gutters, are that the minimum top width of a valley gutter should be 500 mm, and that of a parapet and boundary-wall gutter 300 mm, and that the overall depth of the gutter should allow a freeboard of two-sevenths of the maximum depth of flow in the gutter, with an upper limit of 75 mm.

As is the case with the channel of a highway drainage system, the outlets from a roof gutter divide the gutter into segments, all behaving as independent channels. From the hydraulic point of view, the optimum arrangement for the outlets is when they are equally spaced (Fig. 10.1), each having a discharge capacity

$$Q = \frac{\Sigma Q}{n}$$

where ΣQ is the total volume of flow from the roof. If there are only two outlets (Fig. 10.1(b)), then each outlet carries half the total flow, and the capacity requirement of the channel is a quarter of the total flow. In practice,

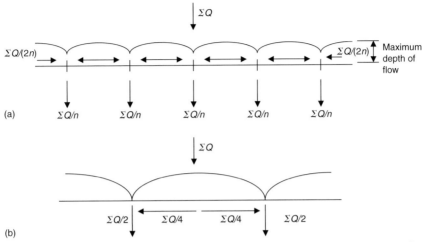

Figure 10.1 *Flow in a roof gutter. (a) Roof gutter with a series of outlets (number of outlets = n), (b) Roof gutter with two outlets.*

however, the number and position of the outlets are often determined by the layout and architecture of the building.

The two most common types of outlets are:

(*a*) A rain-pipe connected directly to the sole of the gutter. Eaves gutters are usually provided with this type of outlet.
(*b*) A box receiver into which the gutter discharges the flow, and from which the flow passes on to the rain-pipe. This method is preferable as the box receiver acts as a mini tank into which the flow from the gutter is discharged freely.

10.4   Capacities of roof gutters

The capacities of all types of roof gutters are based on the assumption that the flow from the gutter is discharged freely. From the point of view of the analysis, this means that the specific energy of flow at the outlet is minimum, that is, the flow is critical. This is verified in Examples 10.2 and 10.3.

10.4.1   Capacities of truly half-round eaves gutters

Applying the procedure outlined above, the capacities of eaves gutters of truly semicircular shapes are obtained for $n = 0{\cdot}011$, and $n = 0$ (see Table 10.1). It is interesting to note that the capacity of a channel, laid horizontally, and with friction ignored, is independent of the length of the channel.

Table 10.1 *Capacities of standard eaves gutters (l/s) obtained from varied flow theory*

Gutter size (mm)	$n = 0.011$					$n = 0$
	$L = 2\,\mathrm{m}$	$L = 4\,\mathrm{m}$	$L = 6\,\mathrm{m}$	$L = 8\,\mathrm{m}$	$L = 10\,\mathrm{m}$	
75	0·492	0·464	0·439	0·418	0·399	0·527
100	1·032	0·989	0·951	0·916	0·885	1·083
115	1·475	1·423	1·374	1·331	1·290	1·534
125	1·824	1·765	1·711	1·661	1·615	1·889
150	2·900	2·825	2·754	2·691	2·627	2·965

Table 10.2 *Capacities (l/s) of standard eaves gutters, before and after applying correction to the values given in Table 1 of reference [1.4]*

Gutter size (mm)	Full capacity	Reduced capacities				
		$L = 2\,\mathrm{m}$	$L = 4\,\mathrm{m}$	$L = 6\,\mathrm{m}$	$L = 8\,\mathrm{m}$	$L = 10\,\mathrm{m}$
75	0·38	0·38	0·35	0·33	0·30	0·30
100	0·78	0·78	0·73	0·73	0·67	0·62
115	1·11	1·11	1·03	1·03	0·95	0·89
125	1·37	1·37	1·27	1·27	1·18	1·10
150	2·16	2·16	2·16	2·01	2·01	1·86

Table 10.3 *Depths of flow at outlets of semicircular roof gutters (mm)*

Gutter size (mm)	$n = 0.011$					$n = 0$
	$L = 2\,\mathrm{m}$	$L = 4\,\mathrm{m}$	$L = 6\,\mathrm{m}$	$L = 8\,\mathrm{m}$	$L = 10\,\mathrm{m}$	
75	23·72	23·00	22·36	21·80	21·27	24·56
100	31·98	31·28	30·65	30·06	29·52	32·77
115	36·91	36·23	35·59	35·00	34·45	37·66
125	40·20	39·53	38·90	38·31	37·76	40·94
150	48·44	47·79	47·16	46·61	46·03	49·13

It therefore coincides with that of a channel with zero length. Table 10.2 shows capacities given in reference [10.4], but reduced according to the ratios of lengths to the depth of water. The depth of flow at the outlet, where the flow is assumed to be discharging freely, is given in Table 10.3. It is evident that the capacities calculated from the varied flow theory are consistently higher than those given in reference [10.4]. This difference in values may be due to the factor of safety inherent in the values given in reference [10.4].

Example 10.2: From a typical set of values taken from Tables 10.1 and 10.3, verify that the flow at the outlet of the gutter is critical.

Solution: Let us consider the 125 mm diameter, 10 m long gutter, with $n = 0{\cdot}011$. The computed rate of discharge and the depth of flow at the outlet are

$$Q = 1{\cdot}615 \, \text{l/s}$$
$$y = 37{\cdot}76 \, \text{mm}$$

From Fig. 10.2, we determine

$$\cos\theta = 1 - \frac{2 \times 0{\cdot}03776}{0{\cdot}125} = 0{\cdot}39584$$

giving

$$\theta = 66{\cdot}6816° = 1{\cdot}1638^R \qquad \sin\theta = 0{\cdot}9183$$

From Eqs (2.8b) and (2.8c)

$$A = \frac{1}{4}(1{\cdot}1638 - 0{\cdot}39584 \times 0{\cdot}9183)(0{\cdot}125^2) = 0{\cdot}003126 \, \text{m}^2$$

$$T = 0{\cdot}125 \times 0{\cdot}9183 = 0{\cdot}11479 \, \text{m}$$

$$D = \frac{A}{T} = \frac{0{\cdot}003126}{0{\cdot}11479} = 0{\cdot}02723 \, \text{m}$$

Also,

$$U = \frac{Q}{A} = \frac{0{\cdot}001615}{0{\cdot}003126} = 0{\cdot}5166 \, \text{m/s}$$

which gives

$$F = \sqrt{\frac{U^2}{gD}} = \sqrt{\frac{0{\cdot}5166^2}{9{\cdot}806 \times 0{\cdot}02723}} = 1{\cdot}0$$

Hence, the flow at the outlet of the gutter is critical.

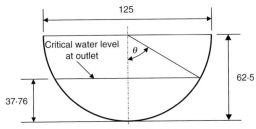

Figure 10.2 *Half-round roof gutter of Example 10.2 (all dimensions in millimetres).*

10.4.2 Capacities of trapezoidal roof gutters

The trapezoidal roof gutters are specified in BS 569 [10.5]. The capacities of these gutters are computed after allowing freeboard of two-sevenths of the overall depth of the gutter. Taking h as the design depth of flow, the capacities are determined using the following dimensions:

Valley gutter (406 mm × 127 mm × 254 mm)

$$B = 254 \text{ mm}$$

$$h = \frac{5}{7} \times 127 = 91 \text{ mm}$$

$$m_1 = m_2 = \frac{406 - 254}{2 \times 127} = 0 \cdot 5984$$

Valley gutter (457 mm × 127 mm × 152 mm)

$$B = 152 \text{ mm}$$

$$h = \frac{5}{7} \times 127 = 91 \text{ mm}$$

$$m_1 = m_2 = \frac{457 - 152}{2 \times 127} = 1 \cdot 2008$$

Valley gutter (610 mm × 152 mm × 229 mm)

$$B = 229 \text{ mm}$$

$$h = \frac{5}{7} \times 152 = 109 \text{ mm}$$

$$m_1 = m_2 = \frac{610 - 229}{2 \times 152} = 1 \cdot 2533$$

North-light valley gutter (457 mm × 152 mm × 102 mm)

$$B = 152 \text{ mm}$$

$$h = \frac{5}{7} \times 152 = 109 \text{ mm}$$

$$m_1 = \frac{1}{\sqrt{3}} = 0 \cdot 5773 \qquad m_2 = \sqrt{3} = 1 \cdot 732$$

Boundary-wall gutter (279 mm × 127 mm × 178 mm)

$$B = 178 \text{ mm}$$

$$h = \frac{5}{7} \times 127 = 91 \text{ mm}$$

$$m_1 = 0 \qquad m_2 = \frac{279 - 178}{127} = 0.7953$$

Boundary-wall gutter (305 mm × 152 mm × 229 mm)

$$B = 229 \text{ mm}$$

$$h = \frac{5}{7} \times 152 = 109 \text{ mm}$$

$$m_1 = 0 \qquad m_2 = \frac{305 - 229}{152} = 0.5$$

Boundary-wall gutter (457 mm × 152 mm × 305 mm)

$$B = 305 \text{ mm}$$

$$h = \frac{5}{7} \times 152 = 109 \text{ mm}$$

$$m_1 = 0 \qquad m_2 = \frac{457 - 305}{152} = 1.0$$

Boundary-wall gutter (559 mm × 152 mm × 406 mm)

$$B = 406 \text{ mm}$$

$$h = \frac{5}{7} \times 152 = 109 \text{ mm}$$

$$m_1 = 0 \qquad m_2 = \frac{559 - 406}{152} = 1.0066$$

Table 10.4 shows the capacities and the depths of flow (in parentheses) at the outlets for these trapezoidal gutters. The values given in reference [10.4] are also shown for in Table 10.4 (column 1). Again, the computed capacities are found to be considerably higher than the corresponding values given in reference [10.4].

Example 10.3: From a typical set of values taken from Table 10.4, verify that the flow at the outlet of the gutter is critical.

Table 10.4 *Capacities of standard trapezoidal gutters (l/s), and depths of flow (mm) at outlets (in parentheses)*

Gutter size (mm) and BS 6367 capacities	$n = 0.005$				$n = 0$
	$L = 5\,\text{m}$	$L = 10\,\text{m}$	$L = 15\,\text{m}$	$L = 20\,\text{m}$	
Valley gutter (406 × 127 × 254) (8·7)	10·95 (54·92)	10·87 (54·66)	10·79 (54·39)	10·81 (54·17)	11·04 (55·19)
Valley gutter (457 × 127 × 152) (6·8)	8·63 (58·66)	8·55 (58·37)	8·48 (58·07)	8·42 (57·85)	8·69 (58·92)
Valley gutter (610 × 152 × 229) (12·7)	16·05 (69·48)	15·96 (69·25)	15·87 (69·02)	15·78 (68·79)	16·16 (69·76)
North-light valley gutter (457 × 152 × 102) (7·6)	9·48 (72·73)	9·40 (72·40)	9·33 (72·11)	9·26 (71·82)	9·56 (73·05)
Boundary wall gutter (279 × 127 × 178) (6·0)	7·61 (54·75)	7·54 (54·43)	7·47 (54·10)	7·41 (53·83)	7·68 (55·05)
Boundary wall gutter (305 × 152 × 229) (9·7)	12·19 (64·54)	12·10 (64·22)	12·02 (63·93)	11·94 (63·57)	12·28 (64·84)
Boundary wall gutter (457 × 152 × 305) (13·4)	16·88 (65·38)	16·77 (65·11)	16·68 (64·88)	16·58 (64·63)	16·98 (65·62)
Boundary wall gutter (559 × 152 × 406) (17·3)	21·85 (64·78)	21·75 (64·59)	21·63 (64·36)	21·50 (64·11)	22·00 (65·07)

Solution: Let us consider the boundary wall gutter 15 m long, with base width 229 mm (see Fig. 10.3). For $n = 0.005$, the computed rate of discharge and the depth of flow at the outlet are

$$Q = 12.02 \text{ l/s} \qquad y = 63.93 \text{ mm}$$

From Fig. 10.3, we determine

$$T = 0.229 + 0.5 \times 0.06393 = 0.261 \text{ m}$$

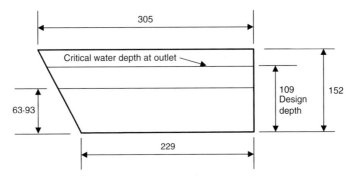

Figure 10.3 *Boundary-wall gutter of Example 10.3 (all dimensions in millimetres).*

$$A = \frac{1}{2}(0\cdot229 + 0\cdot261)(0\cdot06393) = 0\cdot01566 \text{ m}^2$$

$$D = \frac{A}{T} = \frac{0\cdot01566}{0\cdot261} = 0\cdot0600$$

Also,

$$U = \frac{Q}{A} = \frac{0\cdot01202}{0\cdot01566} = 0\cdot7676 \text{ m/s}$$

which gives

$$F = \sqrt{\frac{U^2}{gD}} = \sqrt{\frac{0\cdot7676^2}{9\cdot806 \times 0\cdot06}} = 1\cdot0$$

Hence, the flow at the outlet of the gutter is critical.

10.5 Capacities of almost full flowing circular pipes

In following the procedure described above, it is found that, when the depth is anywhere near the diameter of the pipe, the solution becomes very sensitive. In order to avoid computational difficulties, one has to limit the depth of flow somewhat less than the diameter. As an example, let us consider a circular pipe of 150 mm diameter, and limit the depth of flow to say, 130 mm. The capacities, for channel gradients ranging from zero to 10%, are given in Fig. 10.4.

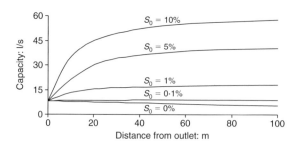

Figure 10.4 *Flow capacity of a 150 mm diameter pipe at various gradients.*

10.6   Capacities of linear drainage channels

As a typical example for the application of the method of computing channel capacities, consider the system unit shown in Fig. 7.6. This system has been proposed for a scheme of urban highway design discussed in Chapter 11. The flexibility of such a system becomes obvious when, for instance, allowance is made for the pedestrians to cross the road, the kerb has to be dropped for a certain length. In such a situation, the channel consists of the base block, the capacity of which is the controlling feature of the design. In the following example, we determine the capacity of the channel when

(a) only the base block is used, and
(b) when the channel consists of both top and base.

Example 10.4: From the dimensions of the linear drainage system used in Example 7.9, determine the capacities of the system for a range of slopes. Take $n = 0.011$.

Solution: We use the dimensions of the equivalent rectangular channel, worked out in Example 7.9, that is,

$$B = 237 \text{ mm} \qquad h = 355 \text{ mm}$$

With these values, we proceed with the computation of flow profiles for various channel gradients from 0% to 5%, limiting the depth of flow to 355 mm. The capacities obtained in this way are shown in Fig. 10.5.
The dimensions of the cross section of flow in the base are

$$B = 261 \text{ mm} \qquad h = 184 \text{ mm}$$

Some of the computed capacities are given in Table 10.5.

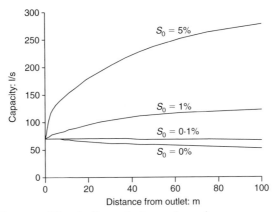

Figure 10.5 *Flow capacities of a linear drainage channel.*

Table 10.5 *Capacities of base of the combined system of Example 10.3 (length of system = 20 m)*

Gradient (%)	0·0	1·0	2·0
Capacity (l/s)	26·30	46·71	58·58

References

[10.1] BEIJ K., 'Flow in Gutters', U.S. Bureau of Standards, Research Paper No. RP 644, Bur. Stand. J. Res., **12**, 1934, 193–213.

[10.2] ESCARAMEIA M., *et al.*, *Hydraulic Capacity of Drainage Channels*, H.R. Wallingford, Report SR 581, November 2000.

[10.3] ANDERSON J.A., 'Linear Drainage Channels for Paved Surfaces', *Highways and Transportation*, March 1997.

[10.4] British Standard BS 6367: 1983, *Code of Practice for Drainage of Roofs and Paved Areas* (Formerly CP 308).

[10.5] British Standard BS 569: 1973, *Asbestos-cement Rainwater Goods*.

11

Design of an urban highway drainage channel

This chapter contains an application of the varied flow theory to the design of a linear drainage channel. The data are taken from a proposed highway drainage scheme. Not all calculations given in the chapter are essential for the designer, but it has been found useful to obtain additional information in order to detect any oddities in the computed values, and to gain confidence in the method of design.

11.1 Description of the problem

Let us now consider a medium-size drainage scheme proposed for an urban highway junction, as shown in Fig. 11.1. The details of the scheme were made available to the author by courtesy of Bradford Metropolitan District Council, West Yorkshire. The drainage is provided by two channels shown by dark lines. One of the channels is along Manchester Road, which slopes from east to west, that is, towards the proposed roundabout (call it Channel A), at an estimated gradient of 1:30 (3·33%), the other channel slopes away from the roundabout (call it Channel B) at 1:74 (1·35%).

The average width of catchment area for the channels are 16 m and 32 m, respectively. Both channels discharge into the existing sewers, also shown in the figure, through the existing gullies. This layout defines the locations of outfalls (marked OF). The access chambers (marked AC) are provided for rodding purposes, and are not involved in the hydraulic design. Thus, the channels are divided into segments of various lengths (see Table 11.1). Both channels are to be constructed in Beany blocks, so they are to be treated as linear drainage channels. It has been suggested that only one standard unit should be used for both channels.

Provision is to be made for pedestrian crossings, so there will be drops in the kerb at suitable places where only the bases, with cover plates, will be

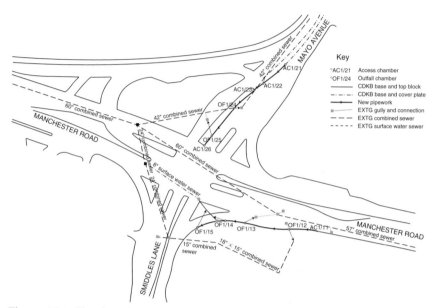

Figure 11.1 *Plan for a drainage scheme at an urban road junction (Bradford, West Yorkshire).*

Table 11.1 *Segments of channels A and B*

Channel A		Channel B	
Segment	Length (m)	Segment	Length (m)
AC 1/11 to OF 1/12	17	AC 1/21 to AC 1/22	18
OF 1/12 to OF 1/13	31	AC 1/22 to AC 1/23	9
OF 1/13 to OF 1/14	18	AC 1/23 to OF 1/24	15
OF 1/14 to OF 1/15	16	OF 1/24 to OF 1/25	26
		OF 1/25 to AC 1/26	8
Total length	**82**		**76**

required (Fig. 11.2), while at other places, the complete unit (top and base) will apply. Preliminary investigations resulted in the selection of the 'Beany block', of the dimensions given in Fig. 7.6. It is required to determine the capacities of the proposed channel of various lengths used in the scheme against the corresponding volume of inflow. The drainage system is to be designed for storm return period of one year.

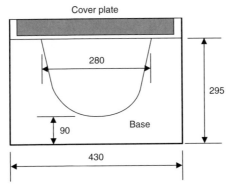

Figure 11.2 *Overall dimensions (mm) of a linear drainage unit consisting of base only (with cover plate).*

11.2   Volume of inflow

The volume of inflow, which is essentially the amount of runoff can be calculated by either of the following two methods:

(a) Using the National Grid Reference 4227E, 4227N (Dewsbury, West Yorkshire), obtain the rate of rainfall corresponding to a time of concentration and the storm frequency (return period). Thus, for an estimated time of concentration of 2·5 minutes, and the storm return period of one year, the intensity of rainfall is found to be 62·9 mm/hr.

(b) Using Eq. (9.2)

$$I = 32 \cdot 7(N - 0 \cdot 4)^{0 \cdot 223}(T - 0 \cdot 4)^{0 \cdot 565}(M_{5-2\,\text{min}})/T \qquad (9.2)$$

For West Yorkshire area, we obtain from Fig. 9.1, $M_{5-2\text{min}} = 3\,\text{mm}$.

Hence we have

$$I = 32 \cdot 7(0 \cdot 6)^{0 \cdot 223}(2 \cdot 1)^{0 \cdot 565}(3 \cdot 0)/2 \cdot 5 = 53 \cdot 24\ \text{mm/h}$$

When the higher value is applied to the entire system, the rate of inflow into the channel running from east to west (length = 82 m) is given by

$$q_i = \frac{62 \cdot 9 \times 16 \cdot 0}{3600} = 0 \cdot 279\,\text{l/s}$$

Hence, maximum discharge carried by the channel (ignoring outfalls) = $0 \cdot 279 \times 82 = 22 \cdot 88\,\text{l/s}$.

For the other channel (length $= 76$ m) the value is $0\cdot509$ l/s. Hence, maximum discharge carried by the channel (ignoring outfalls) $= 0\cdot509 \times 76 = 38\cdot68$ l/s.

11.3 Adequacy of the proposed drainage system

In examining the adequacy of the design of the proposed scheme, the following points need to be considered:

(a) Each channel is to incorporate the 'base only' for a portion of its length. Since, in similar conditions, the capacity of a channel with complete unit throughout its length will be of a higher value than with the base only, the discharge capacity of the system will be represented by the discharge capacity of the base.
(b) The capacity of a channel at a steeper slope is higher than at a shallower slope.

Hence, it will be sufficient to determine whether the capacity of the base at the smaller of the two slopes, that is, at $S_0 = 1/74 = 1\cdot35\%$ is adequate.

11.4 Geometrical properties

The measured dimensions of the equivalent rectangle, taken from Fig. 7.6, are

$B = 0\cdot261$ m
$h = 0\cdot185$ m

Hence, for a full flowing channel, we have

$P = 2 \times 0\cdot185 + 0\cdot261 = 0\cdot631$ m
$A = 0\cdot261 \times 0\cdot185 = 0\cdot048$ m^2

As mentioned earlier, $S_0 = 1\cdot35\%$.

11.5 Roughness factor

The roughness factor n (Manning's n) is based on the average height of roughness (k_s) which is specified as $0\cdot6$ m, that is, from Eq. (5.31),

$$n = \frac{0\cdot0006^{1/6}}{26\cdot3} = 0\cdot011$$

11.6   Channel capacity from the flow profile

The computation of the flow profile for any of the segments, listed in Table 11.1, starts with

(*a*) an arbitrary rate of inflow, and
(*b*) the assumption that the water flows freely at the outfall, that is, the flow at the downstream end of the channel is critical.

The second assumption, which will make the computation start at the downstream end, will be valid if the Froude number at the downstream end is determined as 1·0. Furthermore, if the calculations indicate that the Froude number upstream of the outfall decreases monotonicaly, until its value is zero at the upstream end (where there is no flow), then the flow in the entire segment will be sub-critical (see Table 11.2). If, however, the Froude number varies irregularly then the flow only upstream of a certain location will be sub-critical, and the critical (control) section will have to be located using the procedure described in Chapter 8. For the given configuration, defined by the geometrical properties (section 11.4), it is found that the flow in each segment is sub-critical throughout its length.

Since, the channel is laid at a gradient, the maximum depth of flow will be more than the critical depth (at the outlet), and it will be located somewhere within the reach of the segment. This being so, the initially assumed rate of inflow will have to be adjusted so that the maximum depth equals the available depth of the system, that is 184·0 mm. The corresponding rate of discharge at the outfall will then be the required capacity of the channel. For instance, in the 31 m long channel, the maximum depth occurs 2 m from the outfall (see Table 11.2). When this happens, the adjusted inflow rate is 1·844 l/s/m, and the channel capacity is given by 1·844 × 31·0 = 57·16 l/s (see Table 11.3 and Fig. 11.3).

The computed capacities for all segments are given in Table 11.3.

11.7   Check for time of concentration

The time of concentration T is defined as the sum

$$T = T_s + T_g$$

where T_s is the time taken by water to flow from the furthest point of the catchment to the channel, and T_g is the time of flow in the channel itself. Assuming that $T_s = 2·0$ minutes, the time of concentration of 2·5 minutes,

Table 11.2 *Flow and velocity profiles in the 31 m channel and Froude numbers along the channel*

Distance from upstream end (m)	Depth of flow y (mm)	Velocity U (m/s)	Froude number
0	45·0	0·000	0·00
1	55·9	0·126	0·17
2	63·2	0·222	0·28
3	69·4	0·305	0·37
5	83·2	0·425	0·47
7	95·3	0·519	0·54
9	106·3	0·598	0·59
11	116·6	0·667	0·62
13	126·3	0·727	0·65
15	135·5	0·782	0·68
17	144·3	0·832	0·70
19	152·8	0·879	0·72
21	162·7	0·923	0·73
23	168·3	0·965	0·75
25	175·2	1·008	0·77
27	180·8	1·055	0·79
28	182·9	1·082	0·81
29	184·0	1·113	0·83
30	183·4	1·156	0·86
31	169·8	1·290	1·00

Table 11.3 *Capacities of channels and time of concentration at various lengths*

Length (m)	Channel capacity (l/s)	Mean velocity (m/s)	T_g (min)	T (min)	Depth at outlet (mm)
8	41·7	0·46	0·29	2·29	137·5
9	42·8	0·47	0·32	2·32	139·9
15	48·2	0·54	0·46	2·46	151·5
16	48·9	0·55	0·48	2·48	153·0
17	49·7	0·57	0·50	2·50	154·5
18	50·3	0·58	0·52	2·52	155·9
26	54·9	0·68	0·64	2·64	165·2
31	57·2	0·74	0·69	2·69	169·8

which formed the basis of the intensity of rainfall, can be checked when the time of flow T_g is calculated from the equation

$$T_g = \frac{L}{U}$$

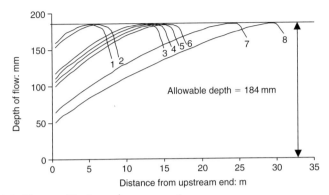

Figure 11.3 *Flow profiles in various segments.*

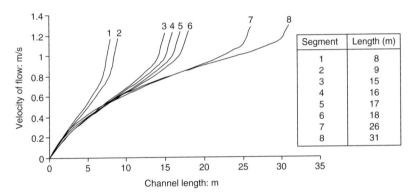

Figure 11.4 *Velocity profiles in various segments.*

where L = length of the channel, and U = average velocity of flow in the channel. The value of U is determined by any of the acceptable methods of averaging the point velocities along the channel length. For instance the values, also given in Table 11.3, are obtained by applying the trapezoidal rule to velocity profiles shown in Fig. 11.4. The corresponding values of T_g, and T are also given in the table. The time of concentration for the largest of the segments is found to be 2·69 minutes. The substitution of this value in Eq. (9.2) gives

$$I = 32{\cdot}7(0{\cdot}6)^{0{\cdot}223}(2{\cdot}29)^{0{\cdot}565}(3{\cdot}0)/2{\cdot}69 = 51{\cdot}97 \text{ mm/hr}$$

This, being less than the assumed value of 62·9 mm/hr, is acceptable.

11.8   Depth of flow at outfalls

Having established that the flow at the outlet is critical, the corresponding depth of flow is determined from Eq. (6.8), that is, for the 31 m segment

$$y_c = \left(\frac{Q^2}{gB^2} \right)^{1/3} = \left(\frac{0 \cdot 0572^2}{9 \cdot 806 \times 0 \cdot 261^2} \right)^{1/3} = 0 \cdot 1698 \text{ m} = 169 \cdot 8 \text{ mm}$$

The values for all segments are given in Table 11.3.

Appendix A

The Newton-Raphson method

A.1 Application of the Newton-Raphson method

The Newton-Raphson method is a powerful technique for producing numerical solutions of equations not amenable to exact solution. The method is described in many text books [A.1, A.2], and can be easily programmed, especially, when the equation is in a single unknown. In describing the method, we bypass the background theory behind the method, and go straight to its application, outlining the route to be followed in the examples worked out in the book.

Let the equation to be solved for y be of the form

$$F(y) = 0 \qquad \text{(A.1)}$$

where the variable F is a known function of y. The Newton-Raphson method starts with an initial trial value y_0 of y, and improves y_0 to a new value so that the value of F gets close to zero within a pre-assigned tolerance. For instance, if the unknown is the depth of flow in a channel, the tolerance may be set not to exceed a fraction of a millimetre. The procedure consists of the following steps:

(a) From the expression for F, determine the expressions for $F(y_0)$ and $F'(y_0)$.

(b) From the equation

$$\delta y_0 = - \frac{F(y_0)}{F'(y_0)} \qquad \text{(A.2)}$$

determine the 'correction' $(\delta y)_{y=y_0}$ to the initial value y_0.

(c) Modify the new value of y_0 to y_1 by adding δy_0 to y_0:

$$y_1 = y_0 + \delta y_0 \qquad \text{(A.3)}$$

229

The steps (*a*) to (*c*) constitute the first iteration. If, after the first iteration, $F(y_1)$ is not sufficiently close to zero, then more iterations have to be carried out by repeating these steps, each time starting with the current value of y. The solution is said to converge if, after an iteration i, the magnitude of the correction δy_i reduces and $F(y_i)$ gets closer to zero. In the computerized version of the method, the solution is set to terminate when δy_i is less than a pre-assigned *tolerance*. It is found that, in most cases where channels of simple geometrical shapes are used, only a limited number of iterations are needed to produce sufficiently accurate results.

It is often helpful to start the solution with a suitable value of y_0. In the examples discussed in the text, trial values are suggested according to the given situations. Let us begin with a relatively simple example of determining the optimum depth of flow in a circular pipe (see section 2.5.3).

The optimum depth of flow in a circular pipe of diameter d (Fig. 2.3), is defined in terms of θ which satisfies the equation

$$F = 3\theta - 5\theta \cos 2\theta + \sin 2\theta = 0 \tag{A.4}$$

The experience suggests a trial value of $\theta = \theta_0 = 150°$ (2·618 radians).

Iteration 1

$$F(\theta_0) = 3 \times 2·618 - 5 \times 2·618 \cos(300°) + \sin(300°) = 0·442$$

$$F'(\theta_0) = 3 - 3 \cos(300°) + 10 \times 2·618 \sin(300°) = -21·17$$

From Eq. (A.2)

$$\delta\theta_0 = \frac{0·442}{21·17} = 0·021 \text{ radians}$$

From Eq. (A.3)

$$\theta_1 = 2·618 + 0·021 = 2·639 \text{ radians} = 151·2°$$

$$F(\theta_1) = 0·003$$

This being sufficiently close to 0, no further iteration is required, and $\theta_1 = 151·2°$ is accepted as the required solution of Eq. (A.4).

A.2   Head loss in a pipe

The head loss in a circular pipe requires the solution of the following equation for ϕ (see section 5.11):

$$F(\phi) = 2 \log(\phi + A_1) + \phi + A_2 = 0 \tag{5.33}$$

where

$$\phi = \frac{1}{\sqrt{\lambda}}$$

As suggested in section 5.11.1, the initial trial value of ϕ is taken as

$$\phi_0 = \log\left(1 \cdot 474R\frac{d}{k_s}\right) \tag{5.39}$$

We now consider Example 5.8 of the loss of head in a 250 mm diameter circular pipe ($k_s = 0.25$ mm), for which the following numerical values were determined:

$$A_1 = 10 \cdot 983 \qquad A_2 = -9 \cdot 218 \qquad R = 1 \cdot 02 \times 10^5$$

From Eq. (5.39)

$$\phi_0 = \log\left(1 \cdot 474R\frac{d}{k_s}\right) = \log\left(1 \cdot 474 \times 1 \cdot 02 \times 10^5 \times \frac{250}{0 \cdot 25}\right) = 8 \cdot 177$$

Iteration 1

$$F(\phi_0) = 2 \log(\phi_0 + A_1) + \phi_0 + A_2$$
$$= 2 \log(8 \cdot 177 + 10 \cdot 983) + 8 \cdot 177 - 9 \cdot 218 = 1 \cdot 524$$

$$F'(\phi_0) = \frac{2}{\phi_0 + A_1} + 1 = \frac{2}{8 \cdot 177 + 10 \cdot 983} + 1 = 1 \cdot 104$$

Therefore,

$$\phi_1 = 8 \cdot 177 - \frac{1 \cdot 524}{1 \cdot 104} = 6 \cdot 797$$

Iteration 2

$$F(\phi_1) = 2 \log(\phi_1 + A_1) + \phi_1 + A_2$$
$$= 2 \log(6 \cdot 797 + 10 \cdot 983) + 6 \cdot 797 - 9 \cdot 218 = 0 \cdot 0762$$

$$F'(\phi_1) = \frac{2}{\phi_1 + A_1} + 1 = \frac{2}{6 \cdot 797 + 10 \cdot 983} + 1 = 1 \cdot 112$$

Therefore,

$$\phi_2 = 6{\cdot}797 - \frac{0{\cdot}0762}{1{\cdot}112} = 6{\cdot}728$$

$$F(\phi_2) = 2\log(6{\cdot}728 + 10{\cdot}983) + 6{\cdot}728 - 9{\cdot}218 = 0{\cdot}0043$$

If we accept this as the tolerance in the value of F, then we do not have to proceed with any further iteration, and ϕ_2 is the required value of ϕ.

A.3   Channel gradient

The gradient of a channel bed is determined by solving the following equation for ψ:

$$F(\psi) = \frac{\sqrt{32gR}}{U}\log(\psi + B_1) + \psi + B_2 = 0 \tag{5.41}$$

where

$$\psi = \frac{1}{\sqrt{S_0}}$$

We next consider Example 5.9 of the bed slope for a trapezoidal channel, for which the following numerical values were determined:

$$B_1 = 1149{\cdot}79 \qquad B_2 = -54{\cdot}115$$

$$\sqrt{32\,gR} = 16{\cdot}245 \text{ m/s} \qquad U = 2{\cdot}0952 \text{ m/s}$$

From Eq. (5.46)

$$\psi_0 = \frac{\sqrt{32gR}}{2U}\log\left(\frac{11{\cdot}7928\,R^2\sqrt{32gR}}{kv}\right) = 42{\cdot}25$$

Iteration 1

$$F(\psi_0) = \frac{\sqrt{32gR}}{U}\log(\psi_0 + B_1) + \psi_0 + B_2 = 0$$

$$= 7{\cdot}7534\log(42{\cdot}25 + 1149{\cdot}79) + 42{\cdot}250 - 54{\cdot}115$$

$$= 11{\cdot}987$$

$$F'(\psi_0) = \frac{\sqrt{32gR}}{U} \frac{1}{\psi_0 + B_1} + 1$$

$$= \frac{7\cdot7534}{42\cdot25 + 1149\cdot79} + 1 = 1\cdot0065$$

Therefore,

$$\psi_1 = 42\cdot25 - \frac{11\cdot987}{1\cdot0065} = 30\cdot34$$

The successive iterations yield:

$$\psi_3 = \psi_2 = 30\cdot3$$

which is, therefore, the converged value of ψ.

A.4   Depth of linearly varied flow in channels

The properties of flow at two neighbouring cross sections of a channel are related by the equation

$$\frac{1}{g}(QU - Q_0U_0) + \overline{S}_f\overline{A}\,\delta x - S_0\overline{A}\,\delta x + (y - y_0)\overline{A} = 0 \qquad (7.15)$$

We assume that the flow properties of one of these sections (indicated by the suffix 0), are known. If distances are measured from the upstream end of the channel, and the section 0 is downstream of the other section, then the *step length* δx is negative, otherwise positive. Translating the properties of both cross sections in terms of their respective depths, Eq. (7.15) reduces to a relationship between the two depths of flow involved, one known and the other unknown. An obvious way forward is to use the Newton–Raphson method to determine the unknown depth (within an acceptable tolerance), taking the known depth as the initial trial value. Having solved this step, the solution for the next step is obtained by repeating the procedure. The procedure is continued until the depth of flow in the entire channel is known. For an accurate method, the step length has to be sufficiently small, say, 1/100th of the channel strength. The location of the starting section, or *the control section*, as it is called, is discussed in Chapter 8, and many examples of the application of the Newton–Raphson method for the computation of flow profiles are given in Chapter 7.

References

[A.1]   PIPES L.A., *Applied Mathematics for Engineers and Physicists*, McGraw-Hill, New York, 1958, p. 116.

[A.2]   STIEFEL E.L., *Numerical Mathematics*, translated by W.C. Rheinboldt, New York Academic Press, London, 1963, p. 79.

Appendix B

The Runge-Kutta method

B.1 Application of the Runge-Kutta method

The Runge-Kutta method is a technique for solving numerically a first-order differential equation. Like the Newton-Raphson method, the Runge-Kutta method has been described in many text books on applied mathematics and numerical analysis [B.1, B.2]. It has been applied to solve the differential equation of varied flow in channels [B.3, B.4]. Again, we limit our discussion here only to the application of the procedure of the fourth-order Runge-Kutta method, as it is called.

Let the differential equation to be solved in the interval $0 \leqslant x \leqslant L$, and the associated initial condition be

$$\frac{dy}{dx} = f(x,y) \tag{B.1}$$

and

$$y(x_0) = y_0$$

If we divide the interval into segments (steps) of reasonably small lengths, the method determines the values of y at the end of each step. Like the Newton–Raphson method, the accuracy of the method depends upon the length of the step, the smaller the step the more accurate is the value of y.

Let the length of the first step, with one end at $x = x_0$ be δx. According to the procedure, the value of y at the other end of the step, where $x = x_0 + \delta x$ is given by

$$y = y_0 + \frac{1}{6}(k_1 + 2k_2 + 2k_3 + k_4) \tag{B.2}$$

where

$$k_1 = \delta x f(x_0, y_0) \tag{B.3}$$

$$k_2 = \delta x f\left(x_0 + \frac{\delta x}{2}, y_0 + \frac{k_1}{2}\right) \tag{B.4}$$

$$k_3 = \delta x f\left(x_0 + \frac{\delta x}{2}, y_0 + \frac{k_2}{2}\right) \tag{B.5}$$

$$k_4 = \delta x f(x_0 + \delta x, y_0 + k_3) \tag{B.6}$$

It is evident that at the outset, when the procedure is applied to solve the equation of varied flow

$$\frac{dy}{dx} = \frac{S_0 - S_f - (2Q/gA^2)(dQ/dx)}{1 - (Q^2/gA^2 D)} \tag{3.15}$$

a difficulty arises: Since the solution must start at the control section, where the Froude number is unity, dy/dx is indeterminate and, as a result, $f(x_0, y_0)$ cannot be determined uniquely. One way to circumvent this situation is to take the following route:

(a) Construct Eq. (7.15), the equation of the step method, and solve it for y at x, using the Newton-Raphson method. From the depth of flow at x, determine the slope of the flow profile at $x = x_0$.
(b) Apply the Runge-Kutta method, Eqs (B.2) to (B.6), starting at $x = x_0$.

As an illustration, consider the rectangular channel of Example 7.3. Starting the solution at $x = 50$ m, proceeding upstream and assuming the length of the first step as 0·5 m, we obtain from the numerical data worked out in the example.

$$x_0 = 50 \cdot 0 \text{ m} \qquad y_0 = 0 \cdot 1308 \text{ m} \qquad \delta x = -0 \cdot 5 \text{ m}$$

$$x = 49 \cdot 5 \text{ m} \qquad y = 0 \cdot 1616 \text{ m}$$

$$f(x_0, y_0) = \frac{0 \cdot 1616 - 0 \cdot 1308}{-0 \cdot 5} = -0 \cdot 0616$$

$$k_1 = (-0 \cdot 5)(-0 \cdot 0616) = 0 \cdot 0308$$

$$x_0 + \frac{\delta x}{2} = 49 \cdot 75 \text{ m}$$

$$Q = 0.02222 \times \frac{49.75}{50.0} = 0.02211$$

$$y_0 + \frac{k_1}{2} = 0.1308 + 0.0154 = 0.1462$$

$$A_0 = 0.15 \times 0.1308 = 0.01962 \text{ m}^2$$

$$R_0 = \frac{0.01962}{0.15 + 0.2616} = 0.04767$$

$$U_0 = \frac{Q_0}{A_0} = \frac{0.02222}{0.01962} = 1.1325$$

$$S_{f0} = \frac{(nU_0)^2}{R_0^{4/3}} = \frac{(0.015 \times 1.1325)^2}{(0.04728)^{4/3}} = 0.01670$$

$$A = 0.15 \times 0.1462 = 0.02193 \text{ m}^2$$

$$R = \frac{0.02193}{0.15 + 0.2924} = 0.04957 \text{ m}$$

$$U = \frac{Q}{A} = \frac{0.02211}{0.02193} = 1.0082 \text{ m/s}$$

$$S_f = \frac{(nU)^2}{R^{4/3}} = \frac{(0.015 \times 1.0082)^2}{(0.04957)^{4/3}} = 0.01256$$

Substituting the following average values (see Eqs (7.13) and (7.14))

$$\overline{S}_f = \frac{S_{f0} + S_f}{2} = 0.01463$$

$$\overline{A} = \frac{A_0 + A}{2} = 0.02078 \text{ m}^2$$

in the expression for f, we obtain

$$f\left(x_0 + \frac{\delta x}{2}, \, y_0 + \frac{k_1}{2}\right) = -0.116$$

which gives

$$k_2 = -0.5 \times (-0.116) = 0.058$$

$$y_0 + \frac{k_2}{2} = 0.1308 + 0.029 = 0.1598 \text{ m}$$

$$A = 0{\cdot}15 \times 0{\cdot}1598 = 0{\cdot}02397 \text{ m}^2$$

$$R = \frac{0{\cdot}02397}{0{\cdot}15 + 0{\cdot}3196} = 0{\cdot}05104 \text{ m}$$

$$U = \frac{Q}{A} = \frac{0{\cdot}02211}{0{\cdot}02397} = 0{\cdot}9224 \text{ m/s}$$

$$S_f = \frac{(nU)^2}{R^{4/3}} = \frac{(0{\cdot}015 \times 0{\cdot}9224)^2}{(0{\cdot}05104)^{4/3}} = 0{\cdot}01011$$

Substituting the following average values

$$\overline{S}_f = \frac{S_{f0} + S_f}{2} = 0{\cdot}0134$$

$$\overline{A} = \frac{A_0 + A}{2} = 0{\cdot}0218 \text{ m}^2$$

in the expression for f, we obtain

$$f\left(x_0 + \frac{\delta x}{2}, \; y_0 + \frac{k_2}{2}\right) = -0{\cdot}0634$$

which gives

$$k_3 = -0{\cdot}5 \times (-0{\cdot}0634) = 0{\cdot}0317$$

$$x_0 + \delta x = 49{\cdot}5 \text{ m}$$

$$Q = 0{\cdot}02222 \times \frac{49{\cdot}5}{50{\cdot}0} = 0{\cdot}02200 \text{ m}^3/\text{s}$$

$$y_0 + k_3 = 0{\cdot}1308 + 0{\cdot}0317 = 0{\cdot}1625 \text{ m}$$

$$A = 0{\cdot}15 \times 0{\cdot}1625 = 0{\cdot}02438 \text{ m}^2$$

$$R = \frac{0{\cdot}02438}{0{\cdot}15 + 0{\cdot}325} = 0{\cdot}0513 \text{ m}$$

$$U = \frac{Q}{A} = \frac{0{\cdot}022}{0{\cdot}02438} = 0{\cdot}9024 \text{ m/s}$$

$$S_f = \frac{(nU)^2}{R^{4/3}} = \frac{(0{\cdot}015 \times 0{\cdot}9024)^2}{(0{\cdot}0513)^{4/3}} = 0{\cdot}0096$$

Substituting the following average values (see Eqs (7.13) and (7.14))

$$\bar{S}_f = \frac{S_{f0} + S_f}{2} = 0{\cdot}01316$$

$$\bar{A} = \frac{A_0 + A}{2} = 0{\cdot}0220 \text{ m}^2$$

in the expression for f, we obtain

$$f(x_0 + \delta x, y_0 + k_3) = -0{\cdot}0567$$

which gives

$$k_4 = -0{\cdot}5 \times (-0{\cdot}56) = 0{\cdot}0283$$

Hence, we obtain from Eq. (B.2)

$$y = 0{\cdot}1308 + \frac{1}{6}(0{\cdot}0308 + 0{\cdot}1160 + 0{\cdot}0634 + 0{\cdot}0283) = 0{\cdot}1706 \text{ m}$$

In order to complete the flow profile for the entire channel, the method is continued with the second step starting at

$$x_0 = 49{\cdot}5 \text{ m} \qquad y_0 = 0{\cdot}1706 \text{ m}$$

the same step length $\delta x = -0.5\,$m may be retained, or changed to an alternative suitable value. The flow profile given in Table B.1 is obtained by

Table B.1 *Flow profiles for the rectangular channel of Example 7.3 obtained from the Runge-Kutta method gradients of 0% and 1·0%*

x (m)	Depth of flow (mm)	
	$S_0 = 0\%$	$S_0 = 1{\cdot}0\%$
2·0	293·8	32·2
4·0	293·7	43·2
6·0	293·4	52·8
8·0	293·0	61·6
10·0	291·8	69·9
20·0	286·7	107·0
30·0	273·6	139·4
40·0	246·2	164·6
45·0	220·3	170·1
48·0	194·1	166·6
49·0	180·2	162·1
50·0	130·8	130·8

maintaining $\delta x = -0.5\,\text{m}$. The table also contains the flow profile corresponding to the channel gradient of 1·0%.

It can be seen that the flow profiles given in Table B.1 compare very well with the profiles for the same channel computed by the method discussed in Chapter 7, and given in Table 7.2.

References

[B.1] STIEFEL E.L., *Numerical Mathematics,* translated by W.C. Rheinboldt, New York Academic Press, London, 1963, p. 168.

[B.2] JEFFREY A., *Mathematics for Engineers and Scientists,* van Nostrand Reinhold, 1985, p. 729.

[B.3] ANDERSON J.A., 'Linear Drainage Channels for Paved Surfaces', *Highways and Transportation,* March 1997.

[B.4] ESCARAMEIA M., *et al.,* *Hydraulic Capacity of Drainage Channels,* H.R. Wallingford, Report SR 581, November 2000.

Index